LEED® GREEN ASSOCIATE™

V4 EXAM

COMPLETE STUDY GUIDE

SECOND EDITION

A. Togay Koralturk

ISBN-13: 978-0994618016 (paperback)
ISBN-10: 0994618018

Printed in the United States of America

CONTENTS

CHAPTER 1   INTRODUCTION TO GREEN BUILDINGS AND SUSTAINABILITY   1

ENVIRONMENTAL IMPACTS OF BUILT ENVIRONMENTS   2

BENEFITS OF GREEN BUILDINGS   3

REGENERATIVE DESIGN   3

TRIPLE BOTTOM LINE   3

GREENHOUSE GAS EMISSIONS, CLIMATE CHANGE AND GREEN BUILDINGS   4

SUSTAINABLE THINKING   5

SYSTEMS THINKING   6

FEEDBACK LOOPS   7

LEVERAGE POINTS   8

LIFE-CYCLE APPROACH   8

INTEGRATED PROCESS   10

CONVENTIONAL BUILDING PROCESS   10

INTEGRATED BUILDING PROCESS IN DETAILS   11

IMPORTANCE OF THE PROJECT'S LOCATION   11

MAIN PRINCIPLES OF THE INTEGRATED PROCESS   12

ITERATIVE PROCESS   12

TEAM SELECTION   14

EVALUATION AND SELECTION OF STRATEGIES AND TECHNOLOGIES   15

IMPLEMENTATION   16

ONGOING OPERATIONS AND MAINTENANCE   18

PHASES OF THE INTEGRATED PROCESS   19

CHAPTER 2   U.S. GREEN BUILDING COUNCIL AND ITS PROGRAMS   21

ABOUT LEED   22

LEED CERTIFICATION BENEFITS   23

OTHER GREEN BUILDING RATING SYSTEMS ACROSS THE WORLD   24

GBCI   24

LEED PROFESSIONAL CREDENTIALS   25

CREDENTIAL MAINTENANCE PROGRAM (CMP)   26

LEED ONLINE   26

CHAPTER 3   LEED GREEN BUILDING CERTIFICATION PROGRAM   29

LEED STRUCTURE OVERVIEW   29

LEED RATING SYSTEMS   32

40/60 RULE   33

LEED RATING SYSTEMS IN DETAILS   34

LEED FOR BUILDING DESIGN AND CONSTRUCTION (LEED BD+C) RATING SYSTEMS   34

LEED FOR INTERIOR DESIGN AND CONSTRUCTION (LEED ID+C) RATING SYSTEMS   36

LEED BUILDING OPERATIONS AND MAINTENANCE (LEED O+M) RATING SYSTEMS   36

LEED FOR NEIGHBORHOOD DEVELOPMENT (LEED ND) RATING SYSTEMS   37

LEED FOR HOMES RATING SYSTEMS   39

LEED RATING SYSTEM EVOLUTION   40

MINIMUM PROGRAM REQUIREMENTS (MPR)   40

PREREQUISITES AND CREDITS   42

PILOT CREDITS   43

POINT ALLOCATION PROCESS   43

IMPACT CATEGORY DEFINITIONS   44

LEED REFERENCE GUIDES   46

CREDIT INTERPRETATION RULINGS (CIR)   46

LEED INTERPRETATIONS   46

ADDENDA   47

LEED CERTIFICATION PROCESS FOR LEED BD+C AND LEED ID+C PROJECTS   47

1. PROJECT REGISTRATION   47

2. APPLICATION   48

3. REVIEW   48

4. CERTIFICATION OR DENIAL   50

LEED CERTIFICATION PROCESS FOR LEED O+M PROJECTS   50

LEED CERTIFICATION PROCESS FOR LEED ND PROJECTS   51

LEED CERTIFICATION PROCESS FOR LEED FOR HOMES   51

LEED VOLUME AND LEED CAMPUS   53

USGBC POLICIES AND APPROVED ABBREVIATIONS   53

CHAPTER 4   INTEGRATIVE PROCESS (IP)   57

INTEGRATIVE PROCESS—CREDIT   57

CHAPTER 5   LOCATION AND TRANSPORTATION (LT)   63

LOCATION   63

SMART GROWTH   64

PROTECTING THE HABITAT BY CHOOSING THE RIGHT LOCATION   65

TRANSPORTATION   66

NEIGHBORHOOD PATTERN AND DESIGN   67

STRATEGIES TO ADDRESS LOCATION AND TRANSPORTATION   68

LOCATION AND TRANSPORTATION CREDITS   **70**

LEED FOR NEIGHBORHOOD DEVELOPMENT LOCATION—CREDIT   70

SENSITIVE LAND PROTECTION—CREDIT   72

HIGH PRIORITY SITE—CREDIT   75

SURROUNDING DENSITY AND DIVERSE USES—CREDIT   77

ACCESS TO QUALITY TRANSIT—CREDIT   80

BICYCLE FACILITIES—CREDIT   82

REDUCED PARKING FOOTPRINT—CREDIT   84

GREEN VEHICLES—CREDIT   86

DOCUMENTING LT CREDITS   89

CHAPTER 6   SUSTAINABLE SITES (SS)   93

SITE ASSESSMENT   94

SITE DESIGN   94

MINIMIZING CONSTRUCTION IMPACTS   96

RAINWATER MANAGEMENT   96

HEAT ISLAND EFFECT   100

SITE MANAGEMENT   102

STRATEGIES TO ADDRESS SUSTAINABLE SITES   104

SUSTAINABLE SITES PREREQUISITES AND CREDITS   **106**

CONSTRUCTION ACTIVITY POLLUTION PREVENTION—PREREQUISITE   106

SITE ASSESSMENT—CREDIT   108

SITE DEVELOPMENT—PROTECT OR RESTORE HABITAT—CREDIT   110

OPEN SPACE—CREDIT   112

RAINWATER MANAGEMENT—CREDIT   114

HEAT ISLAND REDUCTION—CREDIT   116

LIGHT POLLUTION REDUCTION—CREDIT   119

CHAPTER 7   WATER EFFICIENCY (WE)   123

LEED INDOOR AND OUTDOOR WATER USE CALCULATIONS   124

INDOOR WATER USE   125

OUTDOOR WATER USE   127

STRATEGIES TO ADDRESS WATER EFFICIENCY   129

WATER EFFICIENCY PREREQUISITES AND CREDITS   **130**

   OUTDOOR WATER USE REDUCTION—PREREQUISITE   130

   INDOOR WATER USE REDUCTION—PREREQUISITE   132

   BUILDING LEVEL WATER METERING—PREREQUISITE   135

   OUTDOOR WATER USE REDUCTION—CREDIT   136

   INDOOR WATER USE REDUCTION—CREDIT   138

   COOLING TOWER WATER USE REDUCTION—CREDIT   140

   WATER METERING—CREDIT   142

CHAPTER 8   **ENERGY AND ATMOSPHERE (EA)**   **145**

   ENERGY DEMAND   146

   USE OF REFRIGERANTS   147

   ENERGY EFFICIENCY   148

      ENERGY EFFICIENCY FOR HVAC SYSTEMS   148

      ENERGY EFFICIENCY FOR LIGHTING   149

      ENERGY EFFICIENCY FOR APPLIANCES   149

      MONITOR AND VERIFY PERFORMANCE   150

   RENEWABLE ENERGY   150

      TYPES OF ON-SITE RENEWABLE ENERGY   151

      TYPES OF OFF-SITE RENEWABLE ENERGY   152

   ONGOING PERFORMANCE   153

   STRATEGIES TO ADDRESS ENERGY AND ATMOSPHERE   154

ENERGY AND ATMOSPHERE PREREQUISITES AND CREDITS   **156**

   FUNDAMENTAL COMMISSIONING AND VERIFICATION—PREREQUISITE   156

   MINIMUM ENERGY PERFORMANCE—PREREQUISITE   160

   BUILDING-LEVEL ENERGY METERING—PREREQUISITE   163

   FUNDEMENTAL REFRIGERANT MANAGEMENT—PREREQUISITE   165

   ENHANCED COMMISSIONING—CREDIT   167

   OPTIMIZE ENERGY PERFORMANCE—CREDIT   170

   ADVANCED ENERGY METERING—CREDIT   172

   DEMAND RESPONSE—CREDIT   173

   RENEWABLE ENERGY PRODUCTION—CREDIT   176

   ENHANCED REFRIGERANT MANAGEMENT—CREDIT   178

   GREEN POWER AND CARBON OFFSETS—CREDIT   180

CHAPTER 9   **MATERIALS AND RESOURCES (MR)**   **183**

   CONSERVATION OF MATERIALS   184

   ENVIRONMENTALLY PREFERABLE MATERIALS   185

      LIFE-CYCLE ASSESSMENT   186

PRODUCT TRANSPARENCY 187

WASTE MANAGEMENT AND REDUCTION 187

SUSTAINABLE PURCHASING 189

STRATEGIES TO ADDRESS MATERIALS AND RESOURCES 190

MATERIALS AND RESOURCES PREREQUISITES AND CREDITS 192

STORAGE AND COLLECTION OF RECYCLABLES—PREREQUISITE 192

CONSTRUCTION AND DEMOLITION WASTE MANAGEMENT PLANNING—PREREQ. 194

BUILDING LIFE CYCLE IMPACT REDUCTION—CREDIT 196

BPDO: ENVIRONMENTAL PRODUCT DECLARATION—CREDIT 199

BPDO: SOURCING OF RAW MATERIALS—CREDIT 202

BPDO: MATERIAL INGREDIENTS—CREDIT 206

CONSTRUCTION AND DEMOLITION WASTE MANAGEMENT—CREDIT 209

CHAPTER 10   INDOOR ENVIRONMENTAL QUALITY (EQ) 213

INDOOR AIR QUALITY 214

SET MINIMUM AIR QUALITY STANDARDS 214

STOP SECONDHAND SMOKE 215

USE LOW-EMITTING MATERIALS 215

PROTECT THE SITE DURING CONSTRUCTION 216

SCHEDULE CONSTRUCTION ACTIVITIES TO MINIMIZE OCCUPANT EXPOSURE 216

INCREASE VENTILATION RATES 217

MONITOR CARBON DIOXIDE (CO2) 217

IMPLEMENT GREEN CLEANING PRACTICES 217

PERIODICALLY MAINTAIN AND REPLACE AIR FILTERS 218

REDUCE RADON LEVELS 218

INCREASE OCCUPANT COMFORT 219

THERMAL COMFORT 219

DAYLIGHTING 219

DAYLIGHTING SYSTEMS AND DESIGN 220

VIEWS 221

ACOUSTICS 222

LIGHTING CONTROLS 222

TEMPERATURE CONTROLS 223

ERGONOMICS 223

STRATEGIES TO ADDRESS INDOOR ENVIRONMENTAL QUALITY 224

IEQ PREREQUISITES AND CREDITS 226

MINIMUM INDOOR AIR QUALITY PERFORMANCE—PREREQUISITE 226

ENVIRONMENTAL TOBACCO SMOKE CONTROL—PREREQUISITE 229

ENHANCED INDOOR AIR QUALITY STRATEGIES—CREDIT 231

LOW EMITTING MATERIALS—CREDIT   234

CONSTRUCTION INDOOR AIR QUALITY MANAGEMENT PLAN—CREDIT   237

INDOOR AIR QUALITY ASSESSMENT—CREDIT   239

THERMAL COMFORT—CREDIT   241

INTERIOR LIGHTING—CREDIT   243

DAYLIGHT—CREDIT   245

QUALITY VIEWS—CREDIT   249

ACOUSTIC PERFORMANCE—CREDIT   251

CHAPTER 11   INNOVATION (IN)   255

INNOVATIVE STRATEGY   255

EXEMPLARY PERFORMANCE   256

INNOVATION—CREDIT   257

LEED ACCREDITED PROFESSIONAL—CREDIT   259

CHAPTER 12   REGIONAL PRIORITY (RP)   261

REGIONAL PRIORITY—CREDIT   263

CHAPTER 13   LEED® GREEN ASSOCIATE™ EXAM   265

EXAM REGISTRATION PROCESS   265

ELIGIBILITY REQUIREMENTS   265

HOW TO REGISTER FOR THE EXAM?   265

WHERE TO TAKE THE EXAM?   266

EXAM FEES   266

TESTING CENTER RULES   266

SPECIAL TESTING ACCOMMODATIONS   267

ABOUT THE EXAM   267

NO NEED TO BUY ADDITIONAL STUDY MATERIALS   267

THE EXAM   267

EXAM CONTENT   268

EXAM FORMAT   268

EXAM TUTORIAL AND EXIT SURVEY   269

WHAT TO EXPECT AT THE TEST CENTER   269

AFTER THE EXAM   269

EXAM RESULTS   269

PASSING THE EXAM   270

FAILING THE EXAM   270

HOW TO MAINTAIN LEED CREDENTIALS   270

HOW TO KNOW YOU ARE READY   270

HOW TO ACCESS THE DIGITAL RESOURCES   273

APPENDIX A — SUMMARY OF ASHRAE STANDARDS   275

APPENDIX B — IMPORTANT STANDARDS AND PROGRAMS   277

GLOSSARY   281

INDEX   297

REFERENCES   303

CHAPTER 1

INTRODUCTION TO GREEN BUILDINGS AND SUSTAINABILITY

According to the US Environmental Protection Agency (EPA), green building is the practice of creating structures and using processes that are environmentally responsible and resource-efficient throughout a building's life cycle, from siting to design, construction, operation, maintenance, renovation, and deconstruction. This practice expands and complements the classical building design concerns of economy, utility, durability, and comfort. Green building is also known as a sustainable or high-performance building.

Green buildings are more environmentally sensitive, provide more comfort to building occupants, and also remain resource-efficient and high-performance buildings throughout their entire life cycle, but how does that happen? The answer will be explained throughout this book; however, to highlight the major concept of green buildings, we must first observe the natural system.

In the natural cycle, there isn't any waste. Even what we term "animal waste" is actually a sustainable product, which is an organic fertilizer in agriculture that improves plant nutrition and assists the growth of plants. The key factor of animal waste is its sustainability; it is produced by nature and is continuously reused in a never-ending loop. Nevertheless, is the waste of man-made products also like that? Think about a plastic bag, which takes about five hundred years to break down in the environment and creates a great deal of environmental harm during its lifetime.

Now, let us think about the "**built environment**", which refers to all the man-made surroundings that are needed for human activity, from roads, to buildings, to neighborhoods. We use most of the world's resources to develop our built environments, but do they end up like the plastic bag in the previous example, or can they continue sustainably in nature?

Green building is really a system that evolves by continuously enhancing its level of performance in order to get as close as possible to the natural system, which is by far the most efficient system known to man.

ENVIRONMENTAL IMPACTS OF BUILT ENVIRONMENTS

There is not a single building in the world that does not have an impact on the environment. That being said, the way we build can make a great contribution toward reducing this impact.

In the Unites States, buildings account for the following:

- 14% of potable water consumption[1]
- 30% of waste output
- 40% of raw materials use[2]
- **38% of carbon dioxide (CO$_2$) emissions** (this is an important one to know)
- 24% to 50% of energy use
- 72% of electricity consumption[3]

Accounting for 38% of carbon dioxide emissions, buildings are on top of the list and produce even more carbon dioxide (CO$_2$) than transportation and industrial emitters. And all the built environment contributes to 67% of all greenhouse gas emissions.[4]

But why do our buildings harm the environment? First, when we clear the land to make way for a development, the wildlife habitat in that area is destroyed, and the preexisting permeable soil becomes an impermeable surface. Second, we manufacture building products that pollute water and air, release toxic chemicals, and emit greenhouse gases. Furthermore, during the building operations phase, the building consumes energy, which further increases greenhouse gas emissions and adds to the consumption of potable water, which later becomes a waste product. With the commuting of building users and visitors to the building, the use of single-occupancy vehicles results in increased energy consumption and greenhouse gas emissions.

The list of aspects related to environmental impact is seemingly endless.

BENEFITS OF GREEN BUILDINGS

When looking at the statistics of green buildings, a study by the New Buildings Institute found that average energy use intensity of green buildings is 24% lower than typical buildings.[5]

Additionally, a US General Services Administration survey among twelve green buildings states that green buildings have:
- 26% energy use reduction
- 27% higher levels of occupant satisfaction
- 13% lower maintenance costs
- 33% lower carbon dioxide emissions

Occupants of green buildings are exposed to far lower levels of indoor pollutants and are exposed to superior air, lighting, and acoustical qualities than occupants of regular buildings.

According to the US Environmental Protection Agency (EPA), people in the United States spend, on average, 90% of their time indoors.[6] Which means that developing green buildings will make a serious contribution to the health and comfort of the building occupants and their productivity.

REGENERATIVE DESIGN

Regenerative design is an important aspect to mention that can be seen to be one step ahead of sustainable design, which is a type of building design that creates no waste and provides more output than consumed input. As regenerative design projects do not use any more energy than they produce, they are able to return the excess energy to the utility (projects that only use their own generated renewable energy are called **net-zero energy projects**.) In addition to their sustainable features, they can also contribute to the restoration of the lost environment and habitat, thereby taking regenerative design one step ahead of sustainable design.

TRIPLE BOTTOM LINE

All green buildings should establish three components:
- Economic prosperity (profit)
- Social responsibility (people)
- Environmental stewardship (planet)

Those three components are called the triple bottom line. A commitment to the triple bottom line means looking beyond a project's profitability, or considering more than just a project's sustainable features, or social responsibility.

When developing a green building, the main goal is to establish all three components at the same time. A green building should have an increased value, which will result in increased profit, an environmentally friendly design, and should also serve well to its users and the community.

To illustrate the concept, let's assess the triple bottom line of a skylight that will be installed on the roof of an office space. A skylight will reduce the energy consumed by lighting fixtures, which will reduce greenhouse gas emissions. Less energy usage will also mean fewer operating costs for the office building. Also, natural daylight will create a healthier office space for workers.

If we are able to address and achieve all three components of the triple bottom line, why not install the skylight?

GREENHOUSE GAS EMISSIONS, CLIMATE CHANGE AND GREEN BUILDINGS

The primary greenhouse gases in the earth's atmosphere are water vapor, carbon dioxide, nitrous oxide, methane, and ozone. Each of them is essential to absorb and emit radiation, and without them, the average temperature of the earth's surface would be much colder than it is now.

However, with the increasing concentration of carbon dioxide in the atmosphere, which is the result of human activity, the greenhouse gas balance has been disturbed. **This increase has become the number-one cause for global climate change.** As the greenhouse gas emissions increase, an even larger buildup of carbon dioxide occurs in the atmosphere, thus warming the climate further.

As discussed, the built environment contributes to 67% of all greenhouse gas emissions.[4] This comes from building systems and energy use, transportation, water use, changes in the land cover, building products, and construction. Although changing the way we build will play a significant role in reducing greenhouse gas emissions, merely developing green buildings will not be enough. To establish a lower carbon emissions rate, we need to develop green communities as well.

The first thing that a green community should implement is the reduction of the distances that vehicles travel. The buildings in the suburban areas, even if they are green buildings, create greenhouse gas emissions indirectly due to the long distances that people drive every day in order to commute to and from work. Additionally, emissions from transportation make up half of the total emissions associated with the project, which also means that the project location is another critical factor to consider when developing a green building (the LEED for Neighborhood Development rating system is designed to establish green communities, which will be discussed in later chapters.)

Table 1 shows the common sources of greenhouse gas emissions according to their category, which is important to know for exam purposes.

Common Sources of Federal Greenhouse Gas Emissions	
Category	Sources
Scope 1 Energy	Vehicles and equipment
	Stationary sources
	On-site landfills and wastewater treatment
	Fugitive emissions
Scope 2 Energy	Purchased electricity
	Purchased heating/cooling
	Purchased steam
Scope 3 Energy	Transmission and distribution losses from purchased electricity
	Business travel
	Employee commuting
	Contracted solid waste disposal
	Contracted wastewater treatment

Table 1. Common sources of greenhouse gas emissions from federal facilities as called out by Executive Order 13514

Scope 1 energy relates to the direct energy from the <u>owned or controlled sources,</u> scope 2 energy relates to the <u>purchased energy,</u> and scope 3 energy relates to energy sources <u>that are not owned or directly controlled</u>. To illustrate, the energy generated on-site through burning of fossil fuels falls under scope 1 energy, and the resulting greenhouse gas emissions are classified as scope 1 emissions. The electricity bought from a utility company is classified as scope 2 energy, and the resulting greenhouse gas emissions are scope 2 emissions.

SUSTAINABLE THINKING

The green building process is very different from the conventional building process. While the conventional building process focuses on the snapshots of the project, the green building process looks at the project as a whole. There are three major concepts integral to both green buildings and sustainability that are not a part of the conventional building process: **systems thinking, life-cycle thinking,** and **integrated process**.

As all the buildings are composed of different interrelated systems that form a whole, each of them has an impact on the others. Consider a building envelope and an HVAC (heating, ventilating, and air conditioning) system. The insulation level that a building envelope provides will affect the size and operating cost of the HVAC system. The better the insulation, the smaller the HVAC system will be, which will also mean lower operating costs. Meanwhile, a proper waterproofing membrane on the building foundation will protect the foundation and affect the durability of the whole building. This will also result in less humidity inside the building, which will affect both the HVAC system and the health of the building occupants.

The systems of a building include <u>resources</u>, <u>materials</u>, <u>energy</u>, <u>building occupants</u>, and <u>information</u>. The term **systems thinking** refers to the understanding of each and every system of a building while also understanding their relationships and looking at the project as a whole.

The second major concept of sustainable thinking concerns the **life-cycle approach**, which evaluates the entire life of a project, product, or service. For example, when selecting a building product, the project teams need to ask the following questions: What is the raw material of the product? Was it extracted in a responsible manner? How long can the product be used? How much maintenance does it require? What will happen to the product once its useful life ends? Can it be recycled? Does the manufacturing of this product harm the environment?

Integrated process, which is the third major concept of sustainable thinking, emphasizes the importance of connection and communication among all the professionals and stakeholders in the project. To be able to see the big picture, all the different people in the project should act as a single team. The stakeholders, architects, structural engineers, electrical engineers, mechanical engineers, facility managers, etc.—should work collaboratively, starting from the pre-design phase of the project. That way, each team member can understand the perspectives and strategies of the rest of the team. And the collaboration will enable better decisions to be made to create a high-performance building. Let's take a closer look at these three major green building concepts.

SYSTEMS THINKING

The main idea behind systems thinking is to see that the systems in the building do not work in isolation. Actually, there is not a single system in our universe that works in isolation; everything is interconnected. In order to effectively understand systems thinking, we need to understand the types of systems.

There are two types of systems. The first type is the **open system**, which is a system that constantly consumes other items, uses them, and produces waste at the end. A whole city may be an example of this, as it imports food, energy, and products; however, while a city uses products, it also produces waste, often in the form of sewage, pollution, and solid waste, which consequently mark the end of the system. Therefore, there are no **feedback loops** in open systems.

However, in nature, everything is in a loop, and thus no open system exists. Therefore, this is called a **closed system**, which does not produce any waste product at the end. The system continues independently. Think about the water cycle in our world: The sun heats and evaporates the water on the oceans and the seas and then creates water vapor. The resulting water vapor rises on air, which condenses into rain and goes back to the earth's surface. That water then becomes underground water, which again joins the oceans and seas with the flow. This sustainable cycle does not end.

Finding ways to develop closed systems in our buildings will result in creating sustainable buildings. In order to establish that, we need to evaluate the individual elements in addition to their relationships to each other as a whole when designing our buildings. A decision made for an individual element will have a ripple effect that will affect other elements and systems. Remember the example about installing a proper waterproofing membrane on the building foundation that affects the foundation, the durability of the whole building, the humidity level inside the building, the HVAC system, and the health of building occupants.

Understanding the **emergent properties** of systems is also essential in order to better evaluate why we need to form systems. Every system is a composition of its individual parts. Let us take the human body as an example, in which cells form tissues, tissues form organs, organs form the organ systems, and organ systems form humans. A lung is made up of cells; however, having only lung cells together will not do anything. The whole system needs to be there. Certain properties emerge as the result of interaction of individual elements; these are called **emergent properties** of the systems, and only systems can have emergent properties, not the individuals. The breathing function of the lung is the emergent property of a whole successful system. This is why systems thinking requires the creation of emergent properties to achieve rewarding outcomes.

To take the discussion to the next level, we will now examine **feedback loops,** followed by **leverage points**.

FEEDBACK LOOPS

Feedback loops refer to the flow of information within a system that allows the system to take action. There are two types of feedback loops in systems: positive and negative.

A **positive feedback loop** can be summarized as A producing B, which in turn produces more of A. An example of this would be an interest-earning savings account. As the account grows, more interest is earned, which in turn brings further account growth.

In a **negative feedback loop**, a change brings an additional change in the opposite direction. If a room gets warmer than the set temperature, the thermostat will send a signal to the air conditioning, and the air conditioning will stop blowing warm air.

Understanding these feedback loops is crucial for designing sustainable buildings and neighborhoods. With the feedback loops providing the flow of information, the system can take action when there's a problem. Since the positive feedback loops don't stop, they may create problems in the systems if they're unchecked. However, if the positive feedback loops are checked with the negative feedback loops, the system can stop if there is too much of something.

With current technology, both feedback loops can be implemented by the use of sensors, controls, building automation systems, and more. A building automation system can show building management the excess energy usage statistics by tracking the individual consumption of all the building systems. Equipped with only this information, the building management can then respond and try to discover ways to reduce the energy use. This is called the **prius effect**, which means that users can respond to something only if they have real-time information about it.

LEVERAGE POINTS

A small change can yield big changes. In other words, any action taken in a leverage point of the system can bring about significant results in the system. Think about a construction site that is located close to a river that is the main irrigation source of the surrounding farmlands. If the construction site does not take any action to stop sedimentation and pollution resulting from the construction activities, the whole river can become contaminated. This will then contaminate the farmlands, which will result in contaminated foods. However, by taking action to avoid sedimentation and pollution to the river, which is really a small action when considering the outcome, a whole river can be saved that will also result in saving the farmlands and human health.

Being able to see where actions can yield big changes is a very important part of systems thinking. And only by asking questions, project teams can provide insight to move toward sustainability.

LIFE-CYCLE APPROACH

The second major concept of sustainable thinking is the life-cycle approach. Green buildings need a life-cycle approach, and project teams should always look at the big picture by evaluating all phases of the project together rather than merely looking at the snapshots. A life cycle of a building covers location selection, design, construction, operations and maintenance, refurbishment, and renovation or demolition. At the very beginning of the project, project teams need to think about the very last phase of the building, which would be the demolition or complete renovation of the building.

Let's consider a wood-flooring product that is selected to be used in the project. Project teams need to evaluate the raw material manufacturer of the wood flooring. Was the wood extracted in a responsible manner? After cutting trees, does the wood manufacturer plant new trees in order to avoid deforestation?

Then, the project teams also need to consider the cost and durability of the product, and they need to evaluate what can happen to the wood flooring after its useful life. Can it be recycled, or will it become a waste product? This practice, which investigates materials from their extraction to their <u>disposal</u>, is called a **cradle-to-grave approach**.

In order to avoid waste, closed systems should be formed, and a product should become a part of another product, after its useful life, through <u>recycling</u> or <u>reusing</u>. Evaluating products according to this philosophy is called a **cradle-to-cradle** approach, which aims to extend the product lifecycle to avoid waste.

To examine the environmental cost of a product to nature, the energy consumed resulting from a product's manufacturing, transportation, installation, and use should also be evaluated. The total energy consumed in all of these stages is called the **embodied energy**. By way of illustration, think about marble mined in China, manufactured in Europe, brought to the United States for purchase, and then bought for use in a building. The embodied energy of that marble will include all the energy consumed for the extraction, manufacture, transportation, installation at the site, and, finally, disposal. The more embodied energy a product contains, the more it will result in damage to the environment.

When deciding on the products to be used in projects and also to support decision-making of the project teams, the life-cycle approach should be implemented for environmental considerations with **life-cycle assessment (LCA)**. And for cost considerations **life-cycle costing (LCC)** should be applied.

Life-cycle assessment (also discussed under "Life-cycle Assessment") evaluates all the environmental effects of a product during its whole lifetime. A cradle-to-grave, or cradle-to-cradle, approach is used in LCA, and the total energy use and other environmental consequences resulting from the creation of that material are additionally calculated. Hence, conducting an LCA for the whole building is beneficial in showing the trade-offs between different materials and in helping in the selection of materials that would be the best fit for the project and the environment.

Life-cycle costing assesses a product's total cost by evaluating both its purchase price and its operating costs. For example, a more expensive but more durable refrigeration system can cost less compared to a less expensive but less durable one. If the less durable refrigeration system will require more maintenance and will have a shorter lifetime, using that system may result in more total expenditure for the project owner.

Life-cycle thinking should be applied to all decisions made in green building, not only to product selection. Setting targets and discovering ways to find the best solutions early in the project can yield great results.

INTEGRATED PROCESS

The third and final major concept of sustainable thinking is the integrated process, which is the key to applying sustainable thinking to real-life situations.

Remember the example about the system of the human body, in which the lung is made of lots of cells, but when the cells are put together, without the whole system in place, the cells cannot perform the breathing function of the lung. Without a working system, an emergent property cannot be created.

Assembling the project owner, key stakeholders, architects, civil engineers, and mechanical and electrical engineers will not create a successful project; rather, a system should be formed in which there is a flow of information and collaboration between each member for each phase of the project. To better understand the topic, we will now discuss the conventional building process and then return to explain the details of the integrated building process.

CONVENTIONAL BUILDING PROCESS

In the conventional building process, project teams work in isolation and collaborate when problems occur. Usually, the process starts with a project owner hiring an architectural firm to develop the design. As the design progresses, the architectural firm hires electrical and mechanical designers, who then start integrating the electrical and mechanical parts of the design separately. Then construction plans are issued, and the owner starts the bidding process. In this phase, different general contractors are requested to bid, and once all the bids are submitted, the owner chooses the general contractor and awards the construction of the project. This is called the **design-bid-build** process.

With this approach, the general contractor was not involved in the design phase at all, and furthermore, the general contractor didn't have any collaboration with the architectural firm. In addition, the general contractor didn't have any collaboration with the mechanical and electrical designers. During the construction phase, as problems arise, the general contractor will invite the architectural firm to provide input. In turn, the architectural firm might invite the electrical and mechanical designers to the meetings in order to solve the problems at hand. The outcome of this process will usually be construction delays and extra project costs.

Referring to the human body system example, all the cells were there, but the system was not working.

INTEGRATED BUILDING PROCESS IN DETAILS

To establish an integrated building process, a working system needs to be created. And the system should be active as early as possible during the **predesign phase** or even before deciding on the project location. Think about the following questions:

- How is the climate in the project's location, and what type of heating and cooling system should be installed?
- How should the building be oriented in order to get more sunlight into the building and to reduce the operating costs and provide natural daylight?
- Is there enough rainfall at the location to capture and use rainwater for irrigation?
- What are the goals and requirements of the project's owner?
- How will the building occupants commute once the project is finished, and what are the public transportation options?
- How will the resources and construction materials be transported to the project site?
- What are the building code requirements at the project's location?
- How does energy get to the site?
- What is the type of soil on-site?
- What type of vegetation exists on-site?

They're really the type of questions that should be addressed during the earliest phase of the project. This is why the key in the integrated process is to integrate the <u>whole</u> project team early in order to develop an efficient project design and allow the project team to discover strategies. Taking actions late in the process will only result in delays and additional costs.

IMPORTANCE OF THE PROJECT'S LOCATION

It might be noticed that most of the questions from the previous topic depend on the project's location. To turn the project goals into reality, a strong evaluation of the project location is mandatory. The project location should assist the project teams rather than creating challenges.

The preferred sequence is to set the project goals first and then choose the location that best fits those goals. If the sequencing is vice versa, project teams should still need to discover ways to establish project goals; however, they can also face more problems.

Understanding the whole community is essential for successful project integration. If people need to drive single-occupancy vehicles to commute to a building, the project will generate more greenhouse emissions. The climate in the project location is another factor, which will impact all the building systems. The soil type will also change according to the location, which will affect the whole structural calculation of the building and lead to changes in the whole structural design (for instance, with a weak soil, a building can need a deep foundation; however, this may not be the case with other types of soil.)

Even the level of the underground water for a particular location can make a huge impact on the design and construction of the basement levels, as well as the whole building. When evaluating the site, it is always recommended to work with experts such as engineers, hydrologists, ecologists, and project development consultants. Evaluating zoning and local codes, International Code Council (ICC) standards, Americans with Disabilities Act (ADA) requirements, and all other regulations at that location in the beginning of the project is also essential. Most of the mentioned laws will depend on the project's location, and they will take precedence over LEED requirements. For example, zoning and local codes—not LEED—will determine the building height, type of project to be constructed, size of the building, and minimum parking requirements for a particular location.

MAIN PRINCIPLES OF THE INTEGRATED PROCESS

Below is a list of the main principles of the integrated process:
- **Process matters**: The system should work efficiently.
- **Start early**: The system should be active as early as possible.
- **Follow through**: The commitment should continue throughout the life of the project. It should not end with the completion of construction. This is to ensure that the project strategies are maintained and all the building systems are still efficient through the building operations phase.
- **Look beyond initial costs to long-term savings**: Green strategies have very short payback periods. And project stakeholders should be informed that their project would actually cost less in the long run.
- **Include and collaborate**: The professional project teams should work together with members of the community and always look at the big picture.

To establish a working system among the project team members, stakeholders and member of the community, an iterative process needs to be developed.

ITERATIVE PROCESS

In the integrated process, the ideas are developed by the entire project team. With the discovery of an idea, smaller groups are assigned to research and refine the topic, and then the idea is brought back to the table for the whole team to make the final decision. Hence, an iterative process exists that contains lots of feedback loops in order to establish a working system.

Following is a list of stages for the iterative process:
- Establish clear goals.
- Brainstorm and develop creative and effective solutions.

- Research and refine ideas.
- Explore synergies between different strategies.
- Establish metrics to measure success.
- Set new goals based on the work that has been done.

This approach is unlike the conventional building approach, in which a project team member completes a work individually and then passes it to the next person (which is called a **linear approach.**) To establish an integrative process, it is useful to conduct different types of meetings. Such meetings would include <u>charrettes</u>, <u>team meetings</u>, <u>small task groups,</u> and <u>stakeholder meetings.</u>

Charrettes are intense workshops that are generally held in the beginning of the project and during project milestones. These workshops bring together the entire project team, **facility manager**, and all the stakeholders and outside experts/consultants (the facility manager is the person who will be responsible for running the operations of the buildings after the completion of construction.) Charrettes allow brainstorming and collaboration among different disciplines and experiences. An agenda and list of project goals are discussed in charrettes in order to make important decisions and agree on project goals. With brainstorming and collaboration of the team members, charrettes will also allow the discovery of new project goals. Since charrettes are highly structured, a facilitator is also recommended when conducting charrettes.

Below are the typical stages of a charrette:
- Background briefing: To make sure all participants have the basic information about the project and the topics that will be discussed
- Brainstorming
- Synthesis of work: Discussion of concerns and development of recommendations
- Initial response from the owner or the developer about the discussed strategies and goals
- Follow-up: A written report stating the identified actions that should be sent to all participants

Team meetings will be helpful in discussing strategies among team members from different disciplines. As noted, the design of a building envelope will have a great impact on the building's HVAC system. The level of insulation that a façade provides will affect the heating and cooling loads of the building, which will affect the size and type of the HVAC system to be used in the project. Thus, in a team meeting, the facade designer and MEP designer can work collaboratively to discover the best design solutions for both the facade and the HVAC system.

Small task groups can be held inside each discipline and, together with the involvement of consultants, if they are needed, the groups can explore particular topics, research, and refine ideas. Then, the results can be shared with the whole project team.

Stakeholder meetings are conducted among the project team, stakeholders, neighbors, and community members in order to understand and discuss community needs, issues, and concerns.

It is also essential to involve the facility manager in the building design. Since the facility manager will be responsible for operating the whole building after the completion of construction, facility manager's ideas can result in a better building design and a more efficient building operation phase.

As mentioned, in the conventional building process, a **design-bid-build** approach is used. The construction team is not even a part of the project team during the design phase, and, moreover, the predesign phase does not even exist. However, with integrated project delivery, all the stakeholders, design teams, and construction teams, who really make up the whole project team, work collaboratively from the beginning of the project. This approach is called **design-build**.

TEAM SELECTION

The outcome of the project will depend on the professionals working on the project and the system created. Team members with green building knowledge and experience will make a big impact on the results. LEED Green Associate and LEED Accredited Professional (LEED AP) credentials can be sought in the team members to ensure adequate knowledge.

The duty of a LEED AP project team member is to support and encourage integrated design and streamline the LEED application and certification process. A LEED Green Associate team member will have the general knowledge of green building practices and will provide support to other project team members. (It is very important to remember their duties for exam purposes.) If there are inexperienced people on the team, it will be necessary to provide training and orientation.

There will also be a **LEED Project Administrator** on the team who will be assigned during the LEED project registration and will be the primary contact of USGBC/GBCI for the LEED project. The LEED Project Administrator is a team member who will act as a project manager, overseeing the LEED certification process. (The LEED Project Administrator will also be discussed in more detail under "Project Registration.") To avoid confusion, a LEED Project Administrator does not need to be a LEED Green Associate or a LEED AP. The duties of LEED Green Associates, LEED APs, and LEED Project Administrators in the project are completely different.

EVALUATION AND SELECTION OF STRATEGIES AND TECHNOLOGIES

When the goals are set for the project, there should be a system in place to evaluate the different alternatives. Tools such as life-cycle assessment, life-cycle cost analysis, and computer modeling can all provide great benefits.

Take **Building Information Modeling (BIM)** as an example, which allows the creation of a 3-D project model. With the use of BIM, project teams can model their project in a 3-D model, define the types of materials they plan to use, set the project location, and run energy simulations for the building according to the climate of the project location. Alternatively, the project teams can see how the sunlight interacts with the building and adjust the building orientation in order to maximize the benefits of sunlight, which will result in lower heating and cooling loads. The location of the windows and skylights also can be evaluated from the 3-D model, which can result in providing natural sunlight to the building occupants and a reduction in lighting costs. With the integration of the project schedule to the 3-D model, 4-D construction simulations can be developed, and the project teams can find more effective ways to reduce the total construction duration.

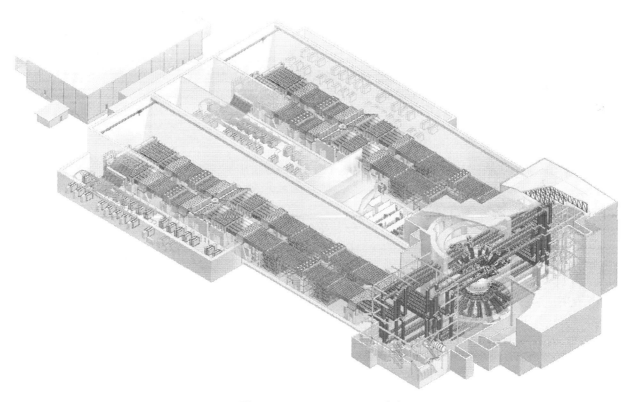

Figure 1. 3D BIM model

The mentioned building energy simulation is a very important tool for achieving LEED certification as well, as there is a LEED "prerequisite" and a "credit" that requires the use of that model in order to show how much energy savings is established by implementing different strategies. (Prerequisites and credits can be thought of as LEED requirements for now, as they will be discussed in depth in the following chapters.)

When doing evaluations about project strategies and technologies, project teams should also refer to the triple bottom line, which is another important aspect for all green buildings.

The phases of the "evaluation" in the integrated process are summarized below:

- Set goals.
- Benchmark performance.
- Identify opportunities for improvement.
- Prioritize and align improvement opportunities with the project goals.
- Implement the program.
- Measure performance and use third-party verification.
- Set new goals or revise goals.

IMPLEMENTATION

Once the design and project planning phases are complete, it is time to turn the green building into a reality by stepping into the construction phase. All the work that was done to that point will make a great contribution to the construction phase, and will both reduce the duration of construction and the total money spent for the project. Documentation in this phase will be very important for compliance with regulatory requirements and achieving a LEED certification.

Let's take a look at some of the main factors that should not be overlooked during construction:

- Prevent air and water pollution by implementing an **erosion and sedimentation control (ESC) plan** that also includes a **stormwater pollution prevention plan** to prevent erosion, sedimentation, and stormwater pollution to the water bodies, wetlands, and entire neighborhood.
- Develop an **indoor air quality management plan** that will protect the indoor air quality for construction workers and building occupants. Typical strategies will include protecting the HVAC system from dust during the construction phase, using materials with minimal levels of toxicity, ventilating the whole building to clear construction contamination before occupancy, and more.

❧ Develop a **waste management plan** in order to address the storage, collection, and disposal of waste generated during the construction phase, which will also address recyclable materials and landfill waste.

The costs during the construction phase will be classified either as soft costs or hard costs. Soft costs cover everything needed for developing a project that does not physically contribute to the building. All the management and supervision costs, design costs, permits, and taxes can be seen as soft costs, and all the other costs that physically contribute to the construction, such as labor costs, construction materials costs, and equipment costs, are hard costs.

Figure 2. A typical landfill (courtesy of Cezary)

Even if construction is completed and both the design and construction teams leave, the integrative process should continue. And in order to continue the integrative process throughout the whole lifetime of a building, the project team needs to be involved in the training and orientation of the building operations personnel, and every single bit of information about the building should be passed on to them.

ONGOING OPERATIONS AND MAINTENANCE

This is the phase in which every project goal, all the assumptions that were made during the design, and the performance of all the building systems should be continuously verified in order to ensure high building performance. In order to establish a successful operations and maintenance (O&M) phase, a system needs to be created with the following activities creating a loop:

1. Audit
2. Plan
3. Measure
4. Adjust and go back to the audit

The LEED O&M certification, which is discussed under the "Rating Systems Descriptions", is all about ensuring an efficient ongoing building performance. Projects need to get recertification every five years in order not to lose their LEED O&M certificate.

The key to understanding whether the building is performing sustainably is to track and evaluate data that the building systems provide. If there's a building automation system in place, the real-time data it provides can show opportunities for energy and water savings and can point out a problem in a particular part of a building. Without such data, it would be impossible to track the operations of buildings. This is the reason why individual energy meters, individual water meters, a building automation system, and tracking devices are needed to successfully operate a building. Additionally, to reveal problems, the following types of inspections can be conducted:

- Retrocommissioning (this is a systematic process for analyzing and optimizing building system performance)
- Energy and water audits
- Solid waste audits
- Occupant surveys
- Green purchasing and green housekeeping program assessments

Orientation and training of the building personnel and occupants should be repeatedly conducted, as tenants and personnel change, and new lessons are learned. Educating building occupants about the green features of the building and sustainable practices can encourage them to participate in sustainable building operations. Continuous feedback from all the building users and personnel is needed to discover potentials for improvement.

The success of the O&M phase will depend on the following principles:

- Start early.
- Find the right team and create the right system.
- Understand the system across time and space.

~ Develop measurable goals.

~ Follow an iterative process to achieve goals.

~ Commit to continuous improvement.

PHASES OF THE INTEGRATED PROCESS

The whole integrated process can be summarized by three main phases:

1. **Discovery phase**: This is the most important phase, which also includes predesign to ensure green building goals are set early and cost-effectively. The risks are identified, and the triple bottom line of the project is assessed. A system is created that enables the efficient collaboration of every participant in the project. The location of the project is well chosen, and applicable codes and standards are evaluated. The level of LEED certification desired and its requirements are thoroughly considered in this phase. Life-cycle costing, life-cycle assessment, and computer modeling of the project are used to evaluate different strategies and alternatives.

2. **Design and construction phase**: The system continues to work, and charrettes, team meetings, small task groups, and stakeholder meetings are continuously conducted. Necessary actions required to protect the construction workers, building occupants, neighborhood, and surrounding environment from construction pollution are taken. The green building goals are turned into reality, with the exception of maintaining them throughout the whole life cycle of the building. All the requirements for LEED certification are documented. The project team conducts both the training and orientation of the building operations personnel.

3. **Occupancy, operations, and performance feedback phase**: The performance of all the building systems should be checked throughout the lifetime of the building. The data that the building systems provide are monitored and evaluated. Orientation and training of the building personnel and occupants are conducted repeatedly as tenants and personnel change and new lessons are learned. Building occupants are educated about the green features of the building and sustainable practices. Continuous feedback from all the building users and personnel is received and the system continues for the whole life of the building.

CHAPTER 2

U.S. GREEN BUILDING COUNCIL AND ITS PROGRAMS

Founded in the early 1990s and based in Washington, DC, the US Green Building Council (USGBC) is a nonprofit organization committed to a sustainable future through cost- and energy-efficient green buildings.

USGBC is made up of tens of thousands of member organizations, chapters, and student and community volunteers. Currently, there are more than 76 chapters, 16,000 member organizations, and 197,000 LEED professionals, and those numbers continue to grow. Members of USGBC include engineers, architects, building owners, contractors, facility managers, building product manufacturers, designers, utility managers, college students, college faculties, government agencies, and more.

USGBC promotes buildings that are environmentally responsible, profitable, and supportive of human health.

USGBC's Mission:

"To transform the way buildings and communities are designed, built, and operated, enabling an environmentally and socially responsible, healthy, and prosperous environment that improves the quality of life."

USGBC's Vision:

"Buildings and communities will regenerate and sustain the health and vitality of all life within a generation."

USGBC accomplishes this mission through the following:

- **LEED:** The most widely known and used green building program across the world.
- **Credentials:** The LEED Green Associate credential and the various LEED AP credentials offer professionals a designation to help them stand out in the building industry.
- **Greenbuild International Conference & Expo:** The world's largest expo, launched in 2002, dedicated to green buildings.
- **Education:** USGBC provides educational programs about green buildings to further spread environmental principles and design.
- **Advocacy:** At every level of government, USGBC provides policymakers and community leaders with all the tools, strategies, and resources necessary to inspire action toward a sustainable built environment.
- **Chapters & Committees:** USGBC contains more than 76 regional USGBC chapter organizations for involvement from the local level to the national level.

The **guiding principles** of USGBC are <u>establishing leadership</u>, <u>promoting the triple bottom line</u>, <u>maintaining integrity</u>, <u>fostering social equity</u>, <u>reconciling humanity with nature</u>, <u>exhibiting transparency, and ensuring inclusiveness</u> (knowing the USGBC's mission, vision and guiding principles is essential for the exam.)

ABOUT LEED

LEADERSHIP in ENERGY and ENVIRONMENTAL DESIGN, in short LEED, is a system developed by USGBC to certify high-performance buildings and sustainable neighborhoods.

The LEED Green Building Rating System™ is a **voluntary, consensus-based rating system** that **provides third-party verification** that a building or community was designed and built to establish energy savings, water efficiency, location efficiency, improved indoor environmental quality, stewardship of resources, and sensitivity to their impacts. LEED addresses all building types through different rating systems and evaluates a building's performance throughout the building's life cycle.

The creation of the LEED green building rating system is led by USGBC member-based volunteer committees, subcommittees, and working groups in conjunction with USGBC staff.

After development, LEED's green building rating systems are subject to review and approval by the LEED steering committee and the USGBC board of directors prior to a vote by USGBC membership.

LEED was created to:

- Define "green building" by establishing a common standard of measurement
- Promote integrated, whole-building design practices
- Recognize environmental leadership in the building industry
- Stimulate green competition
- Raise consumer awareness of green building benefits
- Transform the building market

The number of LEED-certified projects in the United States and around the world is increasing each day. The US General Services Administration required all new federal government construction projects and renovations to achieve at least LEED Silver certification and currently requires these projects to achieve LEED Gold certification.

LEED CERTIFICATION BENEFITS

LEED-certified buildings are proven to be environmentally friendly and to respect human health. However, there are other major benefits of a LEED certification that can be summarized as money savings over the lifetime of a project, increased project value, and increased building occupant satisfaction.

Additionally, LEED projects are known to be much more energy efficient compared with regular buildings and to have lower operating costs. The same thing applies for water consumption, as LEED-certified buildings consume less potable water than regular buildings. LEED-certified projects have an increased building value, which means more return on investment. LEED is a great marketing tool for developers, which results in high occupancy rates. Since the building systems in LEED-certified projects are commissioned during the design and construction phases as a requirement, the building systems create fewer problems during the operations phase. Furthermore, people who work in LEED-certified buildings have increased productivity due to the healthier environment of the buildings, which is the result of increased exposure to natural daylight, increased ventilation rates inside the building, less contaminated indoor air, more open spaces, increased acoustic performance, and many other advantages.

Even though the initial cost of a LEED-certified building may be slightly higher than a regular building (because of the commissioning activities, LEED consulting, and LEED application costs), the life-cycle cost of a regular building typically turns out to be much higher than a LEED-certified building.

OTHER GREEN BUILDING RATING SYSTEMS ACROSS THE WORLD

The following is a list of other green building rating systems across the world:

- **BREEAM** (Building Research Establishment Environmental Assessment Method): A green building rating system developed in the United Kingdom and used primarily in Europe
- **CASBEE** (Comprehensive Assessment System for Built Environment Efficiency): Green building management system in the Japanese market
- **Green Globes™ US/Green Building Initiative (GBI):** A newer rating system that is adapted from Green Globes in Canada
- **GBTool/SBTool:** An online international green building rating system

There is also a growing number of state and local governments that are revising their building codes and standards in order to implement green principles.

The **International Green Construction Code (IgCC)** establishes baseline regulations about the green features of projects and also addresses a building's water efficiency, energy efficiency, site impacts, types and contents of materials used. IgCC is developed by the **International Code Council (ICC),** which is known to develop building codes mainly dedicated to building safety and fire prevention. In addition, local jurisdictions and local building codes started to adopt IgCC codes, which enforce implementation of green principles both in design and construction phases of the projects. <u>When adapted by local jurisdictions or building codes, IgCC becomes enforceable, unlike other green building rating systems.</u>

GBCI

Green Business Certification Inc. (GBCI), formerly known as Green Building Certification Institute (GBCI), changed its name on April 16, 2015; is the sister organization of USGBC that administers LEED building certifications and LEED professional accreditations.

When a project submits all the necessary documents for a LEED application, GBCI is the organization that will review the application and determine if all the requirements set forth in a LEED rating system are fully met or not. And if the requirements are fulfilled, GBCI will grant the LEED certificate.

LEED professional exams are also administered by GBCI, and LEED professional credentials are awarded according to the exam results.

LEED PROFESSIONAL CREDENTIALS

LEED credentials offer professionals a designation to help them stand out in the building industry. Currently, there are three main LEED professional credentials:

- **LEED Green Associate:** GBCI has created the LEED Green Associate credential for professionals who want to demonstrate green building knowledge and expertise in nontechnical fields of practice, to denote basic knowledge of green design, construction, and operations. LEED Green Associates have a proven, up-to-date understanding of green building principles and practices. The <u>LEED GA abbreviation is disapproved by USGBC and cannot be used to demonstrate the LEED Green Associate professional credential.</u>

- **LEED Accredited Professional with specialty:** The LEED AP with specialty credential is created for professionals with advanced knowledge in green building practices and with specialization in a particular LEED rating system. The LEED AP credential is divided into different specialties and each credential is designed to show in-depth knowledge of a particular rating system. Below is the list of all LEED AP specialties:

  a. LEED AP Building Design + Construction (LEED AP BD+C)
  b. LEED AP Interior Design + Construction (LEED AP ID+C)
  c. LEED AP Operations + Maintenance (LEED AP O+M)
  d. LEED AP Neighborhood Development (LEED AP ND)
  e. LEED AP Homes

There is also a LEED AP credential without any specialty, called LEED AP or Legacy LEED AP, which was granted to professionals who passed the LEED AP exam before 2009. The Legacy LEED AP credential is not offered anymore, and all the new LEED APs should choose a specialty.

- **LEED Fellow:** According to USGBC, LEED Fellow designates the most exceptional professionals in the green building industry, and it is the most prestigious designation awarded. Outstanding LEED APs who have demonstrated exceptional achievement in key mastery elements related to technical knowledge and skill are eligible for the honor. LEED Fellows have also made significant contributions in teaching, mentoring, or research with proven outcomes and have a history of exemplary leadership, impactful commitment, service, and advocacy in green building and sustainability.

Other than those mentioned credentials, there are also LEED professional certificates that are needed to become **LEED for Homes Green Raters** or just Green Raters. Green Raters provide **in-field verification** to every LEED for Homes project. (The other rating systems do not require any in-field verification.)

LEED APs or LEED Green Associates may also choose to become **LEED Pro Reviewers** to evaluate the educational LEED courses at **EDUCATION @USGBC**, which is the education portal of USGBC. In exchange, USGBC provides a complimentary yearlong subscription to the USGBC's education portal.

For exam purposes, it's essential to know that the credentialing exams and building certifications are administered by GBCI, not USGBC. LEED Reference Guides, LEED Online, LEED rating systems, and LEED education programs are developed and managed by USGBC. LEED Online is shared by both <u>USGBC and GBCI</u>. And LEED credentials are for people; LEED rating systems are for buildings/neighborhoods. Professionals are accredited; buildings are certified.

CREDENTIAL MAINTENANCE PROGRAM (CMP)

LEED Green Associates and LEED APs with specialty should maintain their credentials by meeting the requirements of the Credential Maintenance Program (CMP) every two years, or otherwise the credential will expire, and retaking the exam will be necessary to maintain the LEED professional credential.

Under the CMP, all the LEED Green Associates must earn **15 continuing education (CE) hours every two years,** and LEED APs must earn **30 continuing education (CE) hours every two years** after earning their credential.

LEED ONLINE

LEED Online is the online platform of USGBC (www.usgbc.org/leedonline/) and is shared by both <u>USGBC and GBCI</u>. In LEED Online, project teams can register their project; pay their certification fees; upload their LEED submittals, documentation, and photos; access their credit templates and calculators; contact their project reviewers; contact customer support; send a credit interpretation ruling (CIR); and more. (A CIR is issued when a project team has questions about the details of a prerequisite/credit; this will be discussed in the "Credit Interpretation Ruling" section.)

For documenting the LEED prerequisites/credits, the project teams should fill in the **credit templates** available at LEED Online. With the use of credit templates, every LEED project prepares LEED submittals in the same format, which streamlines the preparation of LEED applications and the review durations. For the prerequisites/credits that require any calculation, **credit calculators** are also built into the credit templates, which the project teams can use to input their calculation data.

All the project team members can have access to the prerequisites/credits uploaded to LEED Online. LEED Online is used by GBCI as well, since GBCI is responsible for reviewing the submitted documents and granting the LEED certification.

CHAPTER 3

LEED GREEN BUILDING CERTIFICATION PROGRAM

This chapter will explain how a project can receive LEED certification, what the requirements and processes are, and which types of LEED certifications are available. Let's take a closer look at the structure of LEED.

LEED STRUCTURE OVERVIEW

Just like a car rental company categorizing its rental vehicles in categories such as SUVs, minivans, compact cars, standard-sized cars, etc., LEED categorizes projects under LEED **rating systems** according to their types of construction and space usage. For example, a newly built school project may fall under the "LEED Building Design + Construction: Schools" rating system, but a hotel interior renovation project would fall under "LEED Interior Design + Construction: Hospitality" rating system.

The first thing a project team should do is to choose the LEED rating system that's appropriate for its project before registering the project for the LEED certification process. Then the project team can proceed with registering its project at **LEED Online**.

No one can blame a sports car for not handling the road properly on a dusty mountain road. However, an SUV would be required to perform well on mountain roads. Just like we have different expectations from each vehicle category, LEED has different expectations from each rating system in terms of awarding the LEED certification. To summarize, after a rating system is chosen, project teams should basically need to work on fulfilling its requirements.

Let's take a look at the first group of requirements, which are applicable to all the LEED rating systems. In other words, they're applicable to all the projects pursuing LEED certification. They're called the **Minimum Program Requirements (MPR)**. These will also be discussed in the following sections in more depth, but, to summarize, a project must be in a permanent location on existing land, must use reasonable LEED boundaries, and must comply with LEED's project-size requirements. Without fulfilling those three MPRs, a project cannot qualify for a LEED certification, and this is applicable for all ratings systems—period.

After the project complies with the MPRs, it's time to comply with the requirements of the selected rating system. There are two things a project should accomplish under each rating system. The first thing is to satisfy <u>all the</u> **prerequisites** of that rating system. You can think about them as if they're MPRs inside each rating system. <u>Without achieving all of the prerequisites, a project cannot achieve a LEED certification</u>. The second thing a project should do is collect points by achieving the credits of that rating system. A minimum of 40 points out of 100 is required for a LEED certification. (All LEED rating systems are scored on a basis of 100 total points, and 40 points are the minimum number of points to become LEED Certified, which is the base level.) Please note that satisfying prerequisites does not result in the award of any points; only credits do.

Every credit has a different requirement, and every credit awards a point or points. Project teams decide on choosing the credits they want to pursue, preferably during the beginning of the project. There are approximately 70 credits under the LEED Building Design + Construction (LEED BD+C) rating systems and each has different point values. After achieving the chosen credits, the projects need to prepare documentation to show that they achieved their MPRs, the prerequisites, and enough credits, and basically upload that documentation to LEED Online. Done!

To summarize, in order to achieve a LEED certification, first there are the MPRs (just three), which every project must comply with regardless of the rating system. Then there are prerequisites of each rating system that are mandatory to achieve for LEED certification. Then the project team must choose credits to pursue and collect more than 40 points. And all should be documented. Don't forget, all the MPRs and prerequisites are mandatory. However, projects are free to choose the credits they want to pursue.

What if a project satisfies all the MPRs and prerequisites and gets a total of 80 points? Then it will be more than LEED Certified and will be given a LEED Platinum certificate! According to the total number of points a project receives, LEED certification levels are determined:

LEED Certified™: 40–49 points (This is the base certification level.)
LEED Silver: 50–59 points
LEED Gold: 60–79 points
LEED Platinum: 80+ points
(Knowing the points required for each level of LEED certification is essential for the exam.)

However, if a project achieves all the MPRs and earns 90 points but misses only one prerequisite, no LEED certificate will be awarded.

To see the complete list of prerequisites/credits and the point values for credits, it's recommended that you review the LEED scorecard for each rating system from USGBC's website below. (Please review the scorecard carefully, as some features of it can be asked on the exam.):

➤ usgbc.org/resources/LEED-v4-building-design-and-construction-checklist

The LEED scorecard (or LEED Building Design and Construction checklist or LEED project checklist) is an important document, which a project can choose the credits to be pursued and see if the total expected points will be enough to achieve the target level of LEED certification.

For all the LEED BD+C rating systems, the prerequisites and credits are categorized under nine categories, which are called the **credit categories.** (Each credit category will be discussed in depth, starting with chapter 4.) Following are the credit categories:

➤ Integrative Process (1 point)
➤ Location and Transportation (16 points)
➤ Sustainable Sites (10 points)
➤ Water Efficiency (11 points)
➤ Energy and Atmosphere (33 points) **(Category containing the highest points!)**
➤ Materials and Resources (13 points)
➤ Indoor Environmental Quality (16 points)
➤ Innovation (6 points)
➤ Regional Priority (4 points)

Did you notice that there are 110 total points available? Just like some exams have bonus questions, LEED has 10 bonus points. Credit categories for Innovation (6 points) and Regional Priority (4 points) award the bonus points in LEED. But still, every project will be scored on the basis of 100 points, not 110.

LEED RATING SYSTEMS

Just like individuals have credentials such as LEED Green Associate or LEED AP BD+C, all the LEED projects are certified under a single LEED rating system.

All the LEED rating systems are grouped under five broad categories, according to their construction types:

1. LEED for Building Design + Construction (LEED BD+C)
2. LEED for Interior Design + Construction (LEED ID+C)
3. LEED Building Operations + Maintenance (LEED O+M)
4. LEED for Neighborhood Development (LEED ND)
5. LEED for Homes

And under these categories, rating systems are differentiated based on their space usage type in order to address specific needs of different project types:

1- LEED for Building Design and Construction (LEED BD+C) rating systems

   a) LEED BD+C: New Construction and Major Renovation
   b) LEED BD+C: Core and Shell Development
   c) LEED BD+C: Schools
   d) LEED BD+C: Retail
   e) LEED BD+C: Data Centers
   f) LEED BD+C: Warehouses and Distribution Centers
   g) LEED BD+C: Hospitality
   h) LEED BD+C: Healthcare

2- LEED for Interior Design and Construction (LEED ID+C) rating systems

   a) LEED ID+C: Commercial Interiors
   b) LEED ID+C: Retail
   c) LEED ID+C: Hospitality

3- LEED Building Operations and Maintenance (LEED O+M) rating systems

   a) LEED O+M: Existing Buildings
   b) LEED O+M: Retail
   c) LEED O+M: Schools
   d) LEED O+M: Hospitality
   e) LEED O+M: Data Centers
   f) LEED O+M: Warehouses and Distribution Centers

4- **LEED for Neighborhood Development (LEED ND) rating systems**
   a) LEED ND: Plan
   b) LEED ND: Built Project

5- **LEED for Homes rating systems**
   a) LEED BD+C: Homes and Multifamily Low-rise
   b) LEED BD+C: Multifamily Mid-rise

Projects can also choose to use the rating system selector inside LEED Online, which helps project teams choose the most appropriate system for their project.

Some projects may also seem appropriate for more than one rating system. Think about a forty-story high-rise building project that contains a hotel on the first twenty floors and residential units on the floors above twenty. Half of the building can be certified under LEED BD+C: Hospitality, while the other half can be certified under LEED BD+C: New Construction and Major Renovation. But in LEED, <u>projects cannot be divided into different rating systems by section, and the whole project should be certified under one rating system.</u> If more than one rating system seems applicable to a project, the **40/60 rule** will be used to decide on the rating system.

40/60 RULE

This rule is used to choose the appropriate rating system for the project if the project seems to fit under multiple rating systems. In the 40/60 rule, a project should be divided into sections according to the appropriate rating system each section fits. Then, the total floor area corresponding to each rating system should be calculated.

If the total floor area of one of the applicable rating systems is less than **40%** of the project's total floor area, that rating system <u>cannot be used</u>. If the total floor area of one of the applicable rating systems is more than **60%** of the project's total area, that rating system <u>must be used</u>. If it falls between **40%** and **60%**, then the project teams can decide on the rating system to be used for the project.

Let's consider the forty-story high-rise building project example in the previous topic, which contains a hotel on the first twenty floors and residential units on the floors above twenty. Since 50% of the project's total area is appropriate for one rating system and the other 50% is appropriate for the other, the project teams will decide which rating system to use. The project teams can look at the requirements of LEED BD+C: Hospitality and LEED BD+C: New Construction and Major Renovation to decide on the rating system they will pursue. USGBC may ask the project teams to change their rating system if it's not chosen adequately.

LEED RATING SYSTEMS IN DETAILS

LEED FOR BUILDING DESIGN AND CONSTRUCTION (LEED BD+C) RATING SYSTEMS

All types of buildings—whether newly constructed or any type of existing buildings going through major renovations while keeping the core structures of the buildings—will fall under the LEED BD+C category. **Single-family and multifamily homes between one and eight stories will be classified under the LEED for Homes category.**

To be eligible for the rating systems under LEED BD+C, **at least 60%** of the project's gross floor area should be completed by the time of LEED certification, with the <u>exception of LEED BD+C: Core and Shell Development (LEED CS)</u>. (See below.)

a) **LEED BD+C: New Construction and Major Renovation** (LEED BD+C: NC)

This is the most general rating system that addresses design and construction activities for both <u>new buildings</u> and <u>major renovations</u> of existing buildings. For existing buildings, this rating system includes major HVAC improvements, significant building envelope modifications, and major interior rehabilitation.

This rating system is for buildings that do not fall under the other LEED BD+C rating systems described below, which are buildings that primarily serve K–12 education, retail, data centers, warehouses and distribution centers, hospitality, or health care.

b) **LEED BD+C: Core and Shell Development** (LEED BD+C: CS)

This is for projects in which the developer controls the design and construction of the building core and the entire mechanical, electrical, plumbing, and fire protection system. However, it does not involve the design and construction of the tenant fit-out (which is called the core and shell construction). An example would be an office-building project in which the common spaces are constructed by the developer and the tenant spaces are left out, allowing the tenants to construct their own custom designs in their office spaces.

The requirement to be eligible for this rating system is to construct less than 40% of the interior total gross floor area. For all the other BD+C ratings systems, 60% of the project's gross floor area should be completed by the time of LEED certification.

The LEED BD+C: Core and Shell Development rating system is also eligible for **precertification**. Once the developer has established a goal to develop a LEED BD+C: CS project, USGBC will grant a precertification to aid in marketing the project to potential tenants and financiers for the unique and valuable green features of the proposed building. Precertification will be granted after USGBC reviews the early design documents of the project. However, the precertification will not guarantee the LEED certification since the LEED certification will be given at the end of construction, when all the requirements are met.

c) **LEED BD+C: Schools** (LEED BD+C: S)

This is for buildings made up of core and ancillary learning spaces on K–12 school grounds. It can also be used for higher education and nonacademic buildings <u>on school campuses</u>.

d) **LEED BD+C: Retail** (LEED BD+C: R)

This is for retailers such as banks, restaurants, apparel stores, electronics outlets, big-box stores, and everything in between.

e) **LEED BD+C: Data Centers** (LEED BD+C: DC)

This is specifically designed and equipped to meet the needs of high-density computing equipment.

f) **LEED BD+C: Warehouses and Distribution Centers** (LEED BD+C: WDC)

This is for buildings that are used to store goods, manufactured products, merchandise, raw materials, or personal belongings (in self-storage).

g) **LEED BD+C: Hospitality** (LEED BD+C: HO)

This is for hotels, motels, inns, or other businesses within the service industry that provide transitional or short-term lodging with or without food.

h) **LEED BD+C: Healthcare** (LEED BD+C: HC)

This is for hospitals that operate twenty-four hours a day, seven days a week and provide inpatient medical treatment, including acute and long-term care.

LEED FOR INTERIOR DESIGN AND CONSTRUCTION (LEED ID+C) RATING SYSTEMS

LEED ID+C ratings systems apply to projects that are a complete interior fit-out. If a company rents an office building and decides to design and construct the interior office space, the LEED ID+C: Commercial Interiors rating system can be used to LEED-certify the office.

a) **LEED ID+C: Commercial Interiors** (LEED ID+C: CI)

This is for interior spaces dedicated to functions other than retail or hospitality. Think about a LEED-certified core and shell office-building project in which the developer was not involved in the design and construction of the tenant spaces. In this scenario, the tenants may decide to get a LEED ID+C: Commercial Interiors certification for their office spaces, which would only cover the interior fit-out design and construction work.

b) **LEED ID+C: Retail** (LEED ID+C: R)

This is for the design and construction of interior spaces used to conduct the retail sale of consumer goods. It includes both direct customer service areas (showroom) and preparation or storage areas that support customer service.

c) **LEED ID+C: Hospitality** (LEED ID+C: HO)

This is for the design and construction of interior spaces dedicated to hotels, motels, inns, or other businesses within the service industry that provide transitional or short-term lodging with or without food.

LEED BUILDING OPERATIONS AND MAINTENANCE (LEED O+M) RATING SYSTEMS

The greenest building is the one already built. It can take up to eighty years to make up for the environmental impacts of demolishing an old building and constructing a new one, even if the newly constructed building is environmentally friendly.

The LEED O+M rating systems apply to existing buildings that are undergoing <u>improvement work</u> or <u>little to no construction</u>. LEED O+M certifies the operations and maintenance of the building and creates a plan to ensure high-performance building operation. LEED O+M monitors the building's systems (HVAC, electrical, automation systems, etc.) as well as the building's performance.

A LEED ID+C: Commercial Interiors certified office located in a LEED BD+C: CS certified building, can also receive a LEED O+M: Existing Buildings certification. By getting a LEED O+M: Existing Buildings certification, the project gets proof that the ongoing building operations are efficient and building operations are high in performance.

It is important to remember that the LEED O+M rating system certifications expire **every five years**, and in order to keep a LEED O+M certification, a project needs to be recertified every five years. Certifications of the other ratings systems do not expire and do not need a recertification.

a) **LEED O+M: Existing Buildings** (LEED O+M: EB)

This is specifically for projects that do not primarily serve K–12 educational, retail, data center, warehouse and distribution center, or hospitality uses.

b) **LEED O+M: Retail** (LEED O+M: R)

This is for existing retail spaces, both showrooms and storage areas.

c) **LEED O+M: Schools** (LEED O+M: S)

This is for existing buildings made up of core and ancillary learning spaces on K–12 school grounds. It can be used for higher education and nonacademic buildings on school campuses as well.

d) **LEED O+M: Hospitality** (LEED O+M: HO)

This is for existing hotels, motels, inns, or other businesses within the service industry that provide transitional or short-term lodging with or without food.

e) **LEED O+M: Data Centers** (LEED O+M: DC)

This is for existing buildings specifically designed and equipped to meet the needs of high-density computing equipment such as server racks used for data storage and processing.

f) **LEED O+M: Warehouses and Distribution Centers** (LEED O+M: WDC)

This is for existing buildings used to store goods, manufactured products, merchandise, raw materials, or personal belongings (such as in self-storage).

LEED FOR NEIGHBORHOOD DEVELOPMENT (LEED ND) RATING SYSTEMS

This rating system is designed to certify new land development projects or the development of land that contains residential uses, nonresidential uses, or both. The LEED ND rating system is designed to ensure that the developing neighborhood integrates the principles of smart growth, urbanism, and green building.

To illustrate, LEED ND-certified land will probably contain a grocery store, a school, and an office within walking distance of all of its residential units. It will also contain safe sidewalks and host high-performing green buildings, green spaces, bicycle networks, recycling storage spaces, and more.

Being within walking distance of grocery stores or restaurants will reduce vehicle driving and consequently reduce greenhouse gas emissions. Bicycle networks will also help reduce emissions and promote physical exercise. The location and design of the neighborhood will aim to reduce **vehicle miles traveled (VMT)** and also create developments that contain both jobs and services that are accessible by foot or public transit. Cities are increasingly using LEED ND certification to establish greener neighborhoods.

One of the major goals of the LEED ND rating is to reduce **suburban sprawl,** which has lots of consequences for the environment. The term "sprawl" refers to the expansion of populations away from central urban areas into low-density areas. A family deciding to move away from the New York City center to a suburban region, while employed in the city center, can be an example of a work-home situation within suburban sprawl. This scenario will result in commuter driving involving long miles or kilometers, and the increased driving of the family will result in increased greenhouse gas emissions resulting from burning fossil fuels. Additionally, the construction of a new house in a previously undeveloped suburban area will destroy the surrounding habitat.

These are some of the reasons why developments in dense areas like city centers are always more environmentally friendly than developments in suburban areas. To avoid populations moving to suburban areas, LEED ND aims to construct better neighborhoods. LEED ND contains two ratings systems:

a) **LEED ND: Plan**

This is for neighborhood-scale projects that are currently in any phase of planning and design and up to 75% constructed. This was designed to help developers market and fund the project among prospective tenants, financiers, and public officials by affirming the intended sustainability strategies.

b) **LEED ND: Built Project**

This is for neighborhood-scale projects that are near completion or were completed within the last three years.

Since LEED ND is about certifying land rather than buildings, it has different requirements. In other words, LEED ND projects are addressed by different credit categories than LEED BD+C credit categories.

All the LEED ND certified lands must address the following credit categories:

- **Smart Location and Linkage**: Promotes the consideration by communities of location, transportation alternatives, and preservation of sensitive lands while also discouraging sprawl.
- **Neighborhood Pattern and Design**: This promotes the development of vibrant, equitable communities that are healthy, walkable, and mixed-use.
- **Green Infrastructure and Buildings**: This promotes the design and construction of buildings and infrastructure that use less energy and water. It encourages more sustainable use of materials and the reuse of existing and historic structures.
- **Innovation and Design**: This recognizes exemplary and innovative performance reaching beyond the existing credits in the rating system and also recognizes the value of including a LEED AP on the design team.
- **Regional Priority Credit**: This encourages projects to focus on earning credits of significance to the project's local environment.

LEED FOR HOMES RATING SYSTEMS

This rating system category is designed to certify single-family and multifamily homes that are between **one and eight stories**. Residential buildings over eight stories should use the LEED BD+C: New Construction and Major Renovation rating system.

The two rating systems under this category are the only rating systems that require **in-field verification**. This means that a Green Rater (also mentioned in the "LEED Professional Credentials" section) is going to conduct a site visit to verify that the home is designed and built to the rating system's requirements.

a) **LEED BD+C: Homes and Multifamily Low-Rise** (LEED BD+C: H)

For single-family homes and multifamily residential buildings that are **one to three stories**.

b) **LEED BD+C: Multifamily Mid-Rise** (LEED BD+C: MR)

For multifamily residential buildings with four to eight stories above grade. Residential buildings with **nine stories or more** should use the LEED BD+C: New Construction and Major Renovation rating system.

LEED RATING SYSTEM EVOLUTION

LEED is updated through a regular development cycle for revisions to the rating system. There are three basic types of LEED development:

- **Implementation and maintenance of current version:** LEED rating systems are continually improved through published updates such as quarterly addenda. (This will be discussed under "Addenda.")
- **LEED rating system adaptations:** Credit adaptations address both specific construction types and international projects, meeting the needs of projects that would otherwise be unable to participate in LEED. For example, the "LEED BD+C: Schools" rating system can be seen as a rating system adaptation of LEED for the purpose of serving school projects. **Alternative Compliance Path** (ACP) can be an example of a credit adaptation for international projects. ACPs enable international projects to earn the appropriate prerequisites/credits by allowing them to meet international standards or their local standards instead of United States–based standards. Rating systems are also periodically updated to cover more ACPs.
- **Next version of LEED:** Rating systems are evaluated and revised periodically. LEED v5 will be the next version of LEED.

Additionally, the LEED Pilot Credit Library (also mentioned under "Pilot Credits") plays an important role in the evolution of LEED. Pilot credits are tested across all rating system types and credit categories and include credits proposed for the next version of LEED. Project teams can pursue any of these pilot credits under the Innovation credit category and earn points by providing USGBC with feedback on the credit. With these feedbacks, USGBC refines the pilot credits and worthwhile credits, which are then added as actual credits to the new LEED rating system.

MINIMUM PROGRAM REQUIREMENTS (MPR)

The minimum program requirements are the minimum standards/characteristics that every LEED project should meet to pursue LEED certification. MPRs state whether a project can pursue LEED certification or not. They provide guidance on the types of projects that are eligible for LEED certification, protect the integrity of the LEED program, and reduce the number of issues that arise during the certification process. They define the types of buildings, spaces, and neighborhoods that a LEED rating system is designed to evaluate. (It is very important to know the MPRs for the exam purposes.)

There are three MPRs:

1) Every project must be in a permanent location on existing land

A project that is designed to move at any point in its lifetime is not eligible for LEED certification. Since a significant portion of LEED's prerequisites and credits are dependent on the project's location, the certification is awarded according to that particular location. Prefabricated or modular structures can be LEED-certified as long as they are installed permanently.

It is also important to locate the projects on existing land to avoid artificial landmasses, which can displace and disrupt ecosystems in the future.

2) Must use reasonable LEED boundaries

The LEED project boundary must include all contiguous land that is associated with the project and that supports its typical operations. These will include the landscaping, septic or stormwater treatment equipment, parking, sidewalks, and even more. Any project space cannot be shown to be excluded in order to give the project an advantage in complying with credit requirements.

In addition, the gross floor area of the LEED project should not be less than **2%** of the gross land area within the LEED project boundary. The "LEED project boundary" is defined by the platted property line of the project, including all land and water within it.

3) Must comply with project size requirements

All LEED projects must meet the following size requirements according to their rating system:

<u>LEED BD+C and LEED O+M rating systems</u>: The project must include a minimum of 1,000 square feet (93 square meters) of gross floor area.

<u>LEED ID+C rating systems</u>: The project must include a minimum of 250 square feet (22 square meters) of gross floor area.

<u>LEED for Neighborhood Development rating systems</u>: The project should contain at least two habitable buildings and be no larger than 1,500 acres.

<u>LEED for Homes</u>: The project must be defined as a "dwelling unit" by all applicable codes. A dwelling unit should include permanent provisions for living, sleeping, eating, cooking, and sanitation. The LEED for Homes rating system additionally refers to the LEED for Homes Scope and Eligibility Guidelines as well for extra requirements.

PREREQUISITES AND CREDITS

Whether deciding to pursue LEED certification or not, all project teams should first take a look at the MPRs to see if their project can be eligible for a LEED certification. Then the project teams will need to determine the rating system that their project fits into. After the rating system is selected, project teams should evaluate the prerequisites and credits of that rating system.

Prerequisites are the minimum requirements that all buildings under a certain rating system must meet in order to achieve LEED certification. For example, all the projects that are certified under the LEED BD+C: Healthcare rating system must meet all the prerequisites of that rating system, while a project registered under LEED O+M: Retail must meet all of its prerequisites. To illustrate, let's take a look at the one of the prerequisites under the LEED BD+C: New Construction and Major Renovation rating system.

Prerequisite—Fundamental Refrigerant Management: Briefly, this prerequisite requires projects not use CFC-based refrigerants in their HVAC&R (heating, ventilating, air conditioning, and refrigeration) systems.

Therefore, every project under the LEED BD+C: New Construction and Major Renovation rating system will not use any CFC-based refrigerants—period. Any project that cannot meet this requirement will not be eligible for a LEED certification. While projects can pick and choose the credits they want to pursue, prerequisites are mandatory. Fulfilling the requirements of prerequisites will also not result in the award of any points.

Now let's look at the **credits**, which are also a part of each rating system. Project teams are free to go for any credit they want within the selected rating system. Each credit has requirements to be fulfilled, and once the requirements are met, the project will earn points. The higher the total points a project earns, the higher the level of LEED certification that will be awarded. To illustrate how a credit works, let's take a look at the one of the credits under the LEED BD+C: New Construction and Major Renovation rating system.

Credit—Access to Quality Transit: Briefly, this credit requires the project to be located within walking distance of public transportation to reduce greenhouse gas emissions resulting from single-occupancy vehicle use.

Hence, any LEED BD+C: New Construction and Major Renovation project located within walking distance of public transportation will earn points under this credit. Projects that do not comply with this credit will not receive any points. As mentioned, there are 100 total points allocated to the credits under each rating system; plus, there are 10 bonus points. A project that earns 50 points total will receive a LEED Silver while another project that earns 80 points will receive a LEED Platinum (if both of them satisfied all the prerequisites and the MPRs).

The prerequisites and credits are also sometimes categorized as **design prerequisites/credits** and **construction prerequisites/credits,** according to the project phase they are performed in. For example, the previously mentioned "Access to Quality Transit" credit is a design credit since the project's location will not be decided during the construction phase.

PILOT CREDITS

Other than the prerequisites and credits, there are also Pilot Credits, which are credits being tested for the updated version of LEED. According to the feedback received by USGBC from the projects that pursue these credits, these pilot credits can become actual credits of the updated LEED rating system, which would be LEED v5.

Pursuing any pilot credit is optional to team members, but if the project chooses to earn a pilot credit, bonus points will be awarded. The points will be awarded under the "Innovation" credit, which is located under the Innovation credit category. (Details will be discussed under the "Innovation" credit.) The pilot credits available to each rating system can be found from the **LEED Pilot Credit Library at;**

- http://www.usgbc.org/pilotcredits

POINT ALLOCATION PROCESS

By looking at the LEED BD+C: New Construction section of the LEED scorecard, it can be seen that each credit contains a different number of points. For example, the Optimize Energy Performance credit contains 18 points while the Site Assessment credit only contains 1 point.

To better understand the system that LEED uses to distribute the 100 total points to each credit, we first need to understand the key elements that a LEED project should accomplish.

Impact Categories, also called **system goals**, are the key elements that every LEED project aims to accomplish. (Knowing the impact categories is essential for the exam.) Impact categories consist of 7 items (don't confuse the impact categories with the credit categories):

1. **Reverse contribution to global climate change**
2. **Enhance individual human health and well-being**
3. **Protect and restore water resources**
4. **Protect, enhance, and restore biodiversity and ecosystem services**
5. **Promote sustainable and regenerative material resources cycles**
6. **Build a greener economy**
7. **Enhance social equity, environmental justice, and community quality of life**

Each credit in LEED will make a contribution to one or more of these impact categories. The more a credit makes a total contribution to each of these impact categories, the more points that credit will contain. To illustrate, let's say that credit A contributes to the following three impact categories at different levels:

- Reverse contribution to global climate change (high contribution)
- Protect and restore water resources (low contribution)
- Build a greener economy (medium contribution)

LEED v4 will determine the total contribution level to each impact category and then calculate the total points that will be allocated to that credit. All the credits in the rating systems contain a minimum of 1 point.

IMPACT CATEGORY DEFINITIONS

According to USGBC, the components of each impact category are summarized as follows:

1. Reverse Contribution to Global Climate Change
- GHG (greenhouse gas) emissions reduction from building operations energy use
- Reverse contribution to global climate change
- GHG emissions reduction from transportation energy use
- GHG emissions reduction from materials and water embodied energy use
- GHG emissions reduction by embodied energy of water reduction
- GHG emissions reduction from a cleaner energy supply
- Global warming potential reduction from non-energy-related drivers

2. Enhance Individual Human Health and Well-Being
- Support occupant comfort and well-being
- Enhance individual human health and well-being
- Protect human health from direct exposure to negative health impacts
- Protect human health globally and across the entire built environment life cycle

3. Protect and Restore Water Resources
- Water conservation
- Protect and restore water resources
- Water quality protection
- Protection and restoration of water regimes and natural hydrological cycles

4. Protect, Enhance, and Restore Biodiversity and Ecosystem Services

- Local biodiversity, habitat protection, and open spaces
- Protect, enhance and restore biodiversity and ecosystem services
- Global biodiversity, habitat protection, and land preservation
- Sustainable use and management of ecosystem services

5. Promote Sustainable and Regenerative Material Resource Cycles

- Reduce raw material resources extraction
- Promote sustainable and regenerative material resources cycles
- Move to cyclical, nondepleting material cycles
- Reduce negative environmental impacts throughout the materials life cycle

6. Build a Greener Economy

- Enhance the value proposition of green building
- Build a greener economy
- Strengthen the green building industry and supply chain
- Promote innovation and integration of green building products and services
- Incentivize long-term growth and investment opportunities
- Support local economies

7. Enhance Social Equity, Environmental Justice, and Community Quality of Life

- Create a strong sense of place
- Enhance social equity, environmental justice, community health, and quality of life
- Provide affordable, equitable, and resilient communities
- Promote access to neighborhood completeness resources
- Promote human rights and environmental justice

For the exam purposes, it is essential to know the components of each category. For example, it is possible to get a question asking the related impact category of "enhance the value proposition of green building."

LEED REFERENCE GUIDES

LEED reference guides are like the law books of LEED, created by USGBC, which defines all the instructions, prerequisite/credit intentions, prerequisite/credit requirements, term definitions, required documentation, and other information necessary to LEED-certify a building.

There is a LEED reference guide for each broad category of the rating systems:

1. LEED Reference Guide for Building Design and Construction (LEED BD+C) v4
2. LEED Reference Guide for Interior Design and Construction (LEED ID+C) v4
3. LEED Reference Guide for Building Operations and Maintenance (LEED O+M) v4
4. LEED Reference Guide for Neighborhood Development (LEED ND) v4
5. LEED Reference Guide for Homes Design and Construction (LEED for Homes) v4

As of November 2013, v4 is the latest version for all the LEED rating systems.

CREDIT INTERPRETATION RULINGS (CIR)

After the project is registered at LEED Online, if a project team has questions about the technical details of a prerequisite, credit, or MPR, a CIR is issued to ask for clarification.

Sometimes the reference guide will not be able to provide all the information regarding the achievement of a particular prerequisite/credit, and, in that case, the project team would submit a CIR through LEED Online and ask for a clarification. One CIR can be sent to clarify a single question, and project teams can submit an unlimited number of CIRs. A CIR has a fixed cost of $220 for both USGBC members and nonmembers.

CIRs are administered by the GBCI, and the Credit Ruling Committee reviews the CIR in two to five weeks, concluding the process by clarifying the question asked.

LEED INTERPRETATIONS

In a process similar to the handling of CIRs, when a project team has questions about the technical details of a prerequisite, credit, or MPR, a LEED interpretation can be issued to ask for clarification. Just like the CIRs, LEED interpretations can be sent using LEED Online.

But the difference between LEED interpretations and CIRs is that LEED interpretations are **precedent-setting,** which means that every LEED project will be able to use it and will also adhere to that LEED interpretation. In other words, the clarification made in the LEED interpretation will be incorporated into the whole LEED rating system. A LEED interpretation will be published online on USGBC's website for general access, and it will be subject to a USGBC consensus-based review, which will take longer than the review of a CIR (approximately three to six months longer).

However, CIRs are not posted online, and they are not applicable to other projects. The <u>fixed cost</u> of issuing a LEED interpretation is $180 more than the cost of issuing a CIR for both <u>USGBC members</u> and <u>nonmembers</u>. <u>CIRs are administered by GBCI while LEED interpretations are administered by USGBC</u>. (That distinction is important to know for exam purposes.)

LEED interpretations can become a part of **Addenda,** which will be the next topic.

ADDENDA

Addenda is the term that combines all the changes, improvements, issued LEED interpretations, and modifications made to a LEED rating system. Just like a piece of software updates itself once a week or so to incorporate the latest updates, LEED rating systems are updated with addendas.

After LEED v4 was released, addenda have been continuously issued at USGBC's website, which combines all the updates made to that rating system through LEED interpretations, modifications, and improvements. In addition, a project that registers with LEED Online after any issued addenda will be automatically subject to that addenda's requirements as well.

LEED CERTIFICATION PROCESS
(FOR LEED BD+C AND LEED ID+C PROJECTS)

1. PROJECT REGISTRATION

The first step for LEED-certifying a building is to register the project through LEED Online, which means completing the registration form and paying the flat registration fee, which is $900 for USGBC members, and $1,200 for nonmembers. In this phase, a **LEED Project Administrator** needs to be assigned.

As discussed, a LEED Project Administrator is the primary project contact for USGBC and GBCI. The LEED Project Administrator is the team member who acts as a project manager, overseeing the LEED project and organizing team members for certain tasks, credits, or prerequisites. The project administrator makes sure the LEED submission is complete and accurate before submitting the project to GBCI for review, and accepts the review results once the review is complete.

2. APPLICATION

After the project registration phase, the project team will identify LEED credits to pursue and assign responsibility for the various credits to project team members. Then the project team will collect information, perform calculations, prepare documentation, fill out the credit templates demonstrating the achievement of the prerequisites/credits, and upload all the documentation to LEED Online. At the end, the LEED Project Administrator will verify that everything is complete, and the project team will pay the review (certification) fees to submit the application.

Review (certification) fees change according to the gross floor area of the project and membership status; it is not a flat fee like the registration fee. Once the review (certification) fees are received, GBCI will start the project review process. (Using credit cards for payments is faster than using checks since the review will not start before the check clears).

3. REVIEW

There are two types of review options for LEED BD+C and LEED ID+C projects. The first option is the **combined review**, in which documentation for all the design and construction prerequisites/credits are submitted for review at the end of the construction phase. At the end of the combined review, GBCI will mark the submitted prerequisites/credits as **awarded** or **denied**. If there is more information needed by GBCI about a prerequisite/credit, GBCI will mark it as **clarify**, and the project teams will submit the requested clarification. It is a little riskier than the second option, which is the **split review**. If some of the expected credits are not awarded, there will not be a makeup since the project is already completed and no change in design or construction can be made. If a prerequisite is not awarded, then the project will not be able to receive a LEED certification at all.

In the second option, **split review**, the design prerequisites/credits are submitted for review during the design phase, and both the additional design prerequisites/credits and all the construction prerequisites/credits are submitted at the end of the construction phase. When the design review is complete, GBCI will either mark the design prerequisites/credits as **anticipated** or **denied**. No prerequisite/credit will be awarded during the design phase since the design will also need to be implemented on-site during the construction phase. If a design prerequisite/credit is marked as **anticipated**, it means that the project will earn it at the end of the construction phase once that design is implemented on-site. If it's marked as **denied**, in order to earn the prerequisite/credit, the project teams will need to come up with a design alternative rather than proceeding with that design. At the end of construction phase, the additional design prerequisites/credits (if applicable) and the construction prerequisites/credits are sent for review. GBCI will this time mark all of them as **awarded** or **denied** unless clarification is needed. If more information is needed about a prerequisite/credit, it will be marked as **clarify**, and the project teams will submit the requested clarification.

The review fees will depend on the gross floor area of the project. Expedited review is also available for an extra flat fee of $10,000 for combined review, and $5,000 per design and construction review under the split review. The fees are flat fees for both USGBC members and nonmembers and will reduce the review duration from 20–25 days down to 10–12 days.

To summarize the review process, let's list all the steps for a combined review and a split review:

<u>Combined review (for LEED BD+C and LEED ID+C projects):</u>
At the end of the construction phase:
1. Both design and construction submittals are sent by the project team.
2. There's a **preliminary review** by GBCI.
3. If additional information is needed to evaluate the application, GBCI will ask for clarifications and the project team will send the clarifications.
4. GBCI will proceed with the **final review** to evaluate the clarifications and to report the <u>awarded</u>/<u>denied</u> prerequisites and credits to the project team.
5. The project team will either accept or appeal the result.

<u>Split review (For LEED BD+C and LEED ID+C projects):</u>
During the design phase:
1. Design submittals are sent by the project team.
2. **Preliminary design review** is conducted by GBCI.
3. If additional information is needed to evaluate the application, GBCI will ask for clarification, and the project team will send the clarification.
4. GBCI will proceed with the **final design review** to evaluate the clarifications and report the <u>anticipated</u>/<u>denied</u> prerequisites/credits to the project team.
5. The project team will either accept or appeal the result.

At the end of the construction phase the following occurs:
6. Both construction and extra design submittals (if applicable) are sent by the project team.
7. **A preliminary construction review is conducted** by GBCI.
8. If additional information is needed to evaluate the application, GBCI will ask for clarification, and the project teams will send the clarification.
9. GBCI will proceed with the **final construction review** to evaluate the clarifications and report the <u>awarded</u>/<u>denied</u> prerequisites/credits to the project team.
10. The project team will either accept or appeal the result.

An unlimited number of appeals can be made for any LEED project. Appeals have a <u>flat</u> fee of $800 for each of the complex prerequisites/credits and $500 for each of the other prerequisites/credits. Expedited review is also available with an additional $500, which will reduce the review duration from 20–25 business days down to 10–12 business days. Being a USGBC member does not reduce the appeal fee. (It is recommended to know that the review fees depend on the gross floor area of the project, while fees for appeals, registration, CIR, and LEED interpretation are flat fees.)

4. CERTIFICATION OR DENIAL

This is the last step of the LEED certification. GBCI issues the final certification report, which will show the level of LEED certification awarded unless the certification is denied. The project teams can again appeal the results if needed, and if no appeals are made, then the project will be deemed **"closed out,"** which means the project team will no longer be able to appeal the certification level or review decisions for specific credits or prerequisites.

As mentioned, the total number of earned points will determine the level of LEED certification, assuming all the prerequisites and MPRs are met.

- LEED Certified™: 40–49 points
- LEED Silver: 50–59 points
- LEED Gold: 60–79 points
- LEED Platinum: 80+ points

This point system applies to all the rating systems in LEED. Any project that earns 80 points will get the LEED Platinum regardless of whether it is a LEED O+M: Hospitality project or a LEED BD+C: Schools project or belongs to any other category.

LEED CERTIFICATION PROCESS FOR LEED O+M PROJECTS

A LEED O+M certification is not granted for good, unlike the case with the other rating systems. A LEED O+M project needs to get recertification **every five years**. And there isn't a split review option available. The LEED O+M project will only have an initial review, which at the end may result in the grant of the LEED O+M certificate. The project will then have recertification reviews every five years to be able to continue its certification. The rest of the certification process is the same with the LEED BD+C and LEED ID+C projects.

LEED CERTIFICATION PROCESS FOR LEED ND PROJECTS

The certification process for LEED ND projects is different from certification of other rating systems due to the lengthy project durations of LEED ND projects, which can even take a decade. After a LEED ND project gets registered and registration fees are paid at LEED Online, there are three stages of LEED ND certification available (Stages 1 and 2 are optional):

- **Stage 1—Conditionally Approved LEED ND Plan** (Optional): Projects can optionally submit their prerequisites to GBCI beforehand in order to verify that they can achieve them. This review is called the **optional prerequisite review** and applies to the prerequisites under the Smart Location and Linkage (SLL) and/or Neighborhood Pattern and Design (NPD) credit categories. (The credit categories of LEED ND projects were mentioned under the segment titled "LEED ND Rating System.") Projects that preapprove their prerequisites will get the status of "Stage 1—Conditional Approval of a LEED ND Plan."

- **Stage 2—Precertified (Reviewed) LEED ND Plan** (Optional): To help projects secure financing or attract tenants before project completion, projects that are under construction or fully entitled can get this stage of certification. This stage of LEED ND precertification is similar to the precertification feature of the LEED BD+C: Core and Shell rating system since precertification is also awarded to aid in the marketing and financing of LEED CS projects.

- **Stage 3—Certified LEED ND** (Required): This is the awarding stage of LEED ND certification if all the requirements have been met. Projects that do not need to pursue Stages 1 and 2 can directly pursue this stage to achieve their certification.

As is the case with the other rating systems, appeals can be made for LEED ND projects at any stage. Expedited review is also available in exchange for extra fees.

LEED CERTIFICATION PROCESS FOR LEED FOR HOMES

Just like all the other LEED rating systems, the first step in certifying a home under the LEED for Homes rating system starts with project registration and payment of the registration fees at LEED Online. However, the process then becomes different from the other rating systems since the LEED for Homes rating system requires <u>in-field verification</u> and <u>performance testing</u> to ensure the rating-system requirements are met on-site. Some activities that take place during the in-field verification may be the on-site verification of modeled building energy performance, on-site verification of the building insulation, on-site air tightness and leakage testings, and more.

At the beginning of the project, project teams will need to hire a **LEED for Homes Provider Organization,** which will be responsible for overseeing all the certification process and incorporate the rating system requirements into the project's design and construction. The LEED for Homes Provider Organization will employ a LEED for Homes Green Rater (mentioned under "LEED Professional Credentials"), who will conduct the in-field verification, and an **energy rater,** who will conduct the performance testing. Energy raters will need to have the **Home Energy Rating System Rater (HERS Rater)** credential, which is an energy rater credential administered by the Residential Energy Services Network (RESNET). Let's take a look at the certification steps of a LEED for Homes project:

1. Registration

- The project is registered at LEED Online and registration fees are paid.
- Project teams select a LEED for Homes Provider Organization.

2. Verify

- Preliminary Rating: The project team, the LEED for Homes Green Rater, and the energy rater will set project goals and the targeted LEED certification level.
- Midconstruction verification visit: The LEED for Homes Green Rater and the energy rater will verify certain building systems while the building walls remain open.
- Final construction verification visit: Once the construction is over, both the LEED for Homes Green Rater and the energy rater will verify that all the rating system requirements have been met. The energy rater will conduct the required performance testing.
- The LEED for Homes Green Rater will complete and submit the LEED for Homes workbook, which is basically a template book that contains all the requested information about the project for LEED certification. A sample workbook can be downloaded from the USGBC's website:

3. Review

- The LEED for Homes Provider will submit the LEED for Homes Workbook to GBCI; the project team will pay the certification fees.
- **Preliminary design review** is conducted by GBCI.
- If additional information is needed to evaluate the application, GBCI will ask for clarification, and the project team will send the clarification.
- GBCI will proceed with the **final design review** to evaluate the clarifications and report the awarded/denied prerequisites and credits to the project team.

≫ The project team will either accept or appeal the result.

4. Certification

≫ GBCI issues the final certification report, which shows the level of LEED certification awarded unless the certification is denied. The project teams can appeal the results if needed, and if no appeals are made, then the project will be deemed "closed out," and the project team will no longer be able to appeal the certification level or review decisions for specific credits or prerequisites.

LEED VOLUME AND LEED CAMPUS

The <u>LEED Volume Program</u> is a streamlined certification process for organizations that plan to certify more than twenty-five prototype-based construction projects within three years. An example of this would be a coffee-shop chain that plans to open up twenty-five coffee shops with uniform designs. Such a project could use the LEED Volume Program to pay lower certification fees to help streamline the certification process.

<u>The LEED Campus Program</u> is not for projects uniform in design, but for multiple projects that are located on a single campus owned by the same entity. An example of this would be a university, planning to construct several educational buildings on the same campus. These projects can use the LEED Campus Program to pay lower certification fees and streamline the certification process.

USGBC POLICIES AND APPROVED ABBREVIATIONS

When using the USGBC logo, the proportions of the original logo's height and width should remain the same. Scaling and no any other alterations can be made to the logo. USGBC should always be acknowledged with use of the logo. The same conditions apply for the use of the LEED logo, and LEED should be acknowledged.

When using the USGBC name on any first reference, it should be written as "U.S. Green Building Council." In subsequent references, the "USGBC" abbreviation can be used. Other naming or abbreviations cannot be used.

<u>The "LEED GA" abbreviation is used commonly everywhere. However, this abbreviation is not approved by USGBC and should not be used. Approved usage is "LEED® Green Associate™."</u>

For the "LEED Accredited Professional®" title, the "LEED AP®" abbreviation can be used, followed by the specialty, which can be written "LEED AP® BD+C" or "LEED AP® Homes."

When describing a LEED certification process, "LEED certification" with lowercase "c" can be used. "LEED-certified" should be used to refer to any project that achieved LEED certification. "LEED Certified" is used to describe a project that has been certified to the base level (for the projects that receive 40–49 points). To describe projects that are certified above the base level, "project X is LEED Gold" or "project X is LEED Silver-certified" or "project is LEED-certified to the Platinum level" can be used.

CHAPTER 4

INTEGRATIVE PROCESS (IP)

INTEGRATIVE PROCESS—CREDIT

- 1 Point

CREDIT SUMMARY

This credit will sound very familiar after having read the integrated process section. The credit awards a point to the projects that implement an integrative process with the fulfillment of the credit's requirements.

As mentioned previously, the collaboration of team members in all the different disciplines is an important aspect in creating successful project outcomes. Every system should be addressed, starting from the predesign phase of the project, by rigorous questioning and challenging of the typical project assumptions.

This credit encourages the coordination of all the project team members, starting from the predesign phase, in discovering unique opportunities for project design, enhanced building performance, and green features.

To earn the credit, the project team will need to conduct preliminary research and analysis for the <u>energy-</u> and <u>water-</u>related systems of the building and also evaluate possible energy and water strategies to achieve the project's goals and the targeted LEED credits. This really means brainstorming and value-engineering the energy-and-water-related building systems beforehand to not only avoid encountering unforeseen conditions but also to find the most effective solutions to meet the project's goals.

CREDIT INTENT

The intent of this credit is to support high-performance, cost-effective project outcomes through an early analysis of the interrelationships among systems.

CREDIT REQUIREMENTS

Starting from the predesign and continuing throughout all the design phases, implement an integrative process among building and site systems that will enable project teams to discover unique opportunities to enhance project performance and environmental benefits. Perform analyses for both the energy- and water-related systems described below:

1. Energy-related systems

Before completing the schematic design, perform a **"simple box" energy modeling** that will enable teams to see the approximate energy use of the building and to evaluate strategies on how to reduce the energy use. A simple box energy modeling is a preliminary building model used to assess the building's energy loads.

Assess at least two strategies related with each of the following:
- Site conditions
- Massing and orientation
- Basic envelope attributes
- Lighting levels
- Thermal comfort ranges
- Plug and process load needs
- Programmatic and operational parameters

An example strategy may be to change the building's base location orientation in order to get more sunlight to the interior spaces so that the lighting energy loads can be reduced.

Or the envelope of the building might be optimized according to the project's location in order to reduce the HVAC loads. And while the project teams look for ways to improve the project performance, they also would need to consider strategies on how to achieve the related LEED credits.

At the end, the project team needs to document how the integrative process informed the design of the following:

- Building and site program
- Building form and geometry
- Building envelope and facade treatments at different orientations
- Elimination and/or significant downsizing of building systems (e.g., lighting controls, HVAC, etc.)
- Other systems

2. Water-related systems

Similar to the "simple box" energy modeling, which shows the building's energy demand, perform a preliminary water budget analysis before completing the schematic design, and calculate the project's water demand. Then look for strategies for reducing the potable water consumption and assess the nonpotable water sources by evaluating the following:

- Indoor water demand (e.g., fixtures and fittings)
- Outdoor water demand (e.g., irrigation)
- Process water demand (e.g., HVAC equipment and washing machines)
- Supply sources (e.g., graywater and rainwater)

The project teams should find at least one nonpotable water source on-site and reduce the burden on the municipally supplied water, or wastewater treatment systems should contribute to at least two of the water-demand components listed above.

At the end, document how the integrative process informed the design of the following:

- Plumbing systems
- Sewage conveyance/on-site treatment systems
- Rainwater quantity/quality management systems
- Landscaping irrigation
- Roofing systems/building form and geometry
- Other systems

As will be discussed in the following pages, LEED has credits tied to the energy- and water-related system items mentioned above. For example, the "Indoor Water Use Reduction" credit will enable the project teams to earn points according to the percentage of potable water reduction they establish.

If a project team decides to pursue this credit, a preliminary water-budget analysis will also be a good starting point to evaluate all the alternatives for reducing the building's potable water demand.

By implementing the integrative process, the project owner will also be informed about the suggested changes while the **owner's project requirements (OPR)**, **basis of design (BOD)**, design documents, and construction documents can be adjusted accordingly. BOD describes the information necessary to accomplish the owner's project requirements, which include system requirements, design criteria, standards, guidelines, etc. developed by the architect/engineer. In order to earn this credit, the project teams will also need to document how the integrative process affected the OPR, BOD, and project design.

KEY THINGS TO REMEMBER

- Project teams are advised to review the ANSI Consensus National Standard Guide 2.0 for Design and Construction of Sustainable Buildings and Communities to implement a successful integrative process.
- Definition of basis of design (BOD).
- Definition of simple box energy modeling.

CHAPTER 5

LOCATION AND TRANSPORTATION (LT)

This chapter will discuss the importance of location and the transportation features of the building and their effects on the green building design. After discussing the LT credit category, the book will go over all the LT credits individually to show how these features are used in LEED certification for a LEED BD+C: New Construction and Major Renovation project. (The LT credit category does not have any prerequisites.)

The Location and Transportation credit category will be discussed under three major sections:

- Location
- Transportation
- Neighborhood Pattern and Design

LOCATION

The location of a green building project should first promote **smart growth,** which refers to the approach that protects undeveloped lands and contributes to developments in projects near jobs, schools, shops, and other destination points with diverse uses.

An example may be a residential project that is located very close to downtown, which also contains several public transportation options.

However, a residential project in a suburban area that requires driving many miles to the downtown area for people to commute would not contribute to smart growth, and that project would hence support suburban sprawl.

There are also other factors to consider when choosing a proper project location. Starting from smart growth, the book will go over all the factors that will contribute to a green building's location.

SMART GROWTH

Suburban sprawl has lots of consequences to the environment. First, the construction of a building on undeveloped land will destroy the habitat and wildlife in that location. Second, suburban sprawl will result in car dependency, which will further damage the environment with the greenhouse gases created. In addition, after people start moving to suburban areas, the cities will need to provide infrastructure to the suburban areas, which will create additional consequences for the environment.

Principles of smart growth are:
- Protect undeveloped land (undeveloped land is also called **greenfield**)
- Reuse/restore previously developed sites
- Reduce automobile use and promote public transportation
- Develop efficient rainwater management
- Reduce the heat island effect (will be discussed in the next chapter)
- Reduce lighting pollution
- Provide stewardship of nature and the site's surroundings

According to the US Environmental Protection Agency (EPA), in order to promote smart growth and discourage suburban sprawl, the following strategies should be applied[1]:
- Mix land uses (residential, commercial, retail, etc. all on the same land)
- Take advantage of compact building design
- Create a range of housing opportunities and choices
- Create walkable neighborhoods
- Foster distinctive, attractive communities with a strong sense of place
- Preserve open space, farmland, natural beauty, and critical environmental areas
- Strengthen and direct development toward existing communities
- Provide a variety of transportation choices
- Make development decisions predictable, fair, and cost effective
- Encourage community and stakeholder collaboration in development decisions

To promote smart growth, some municipalities offer increased **floor-to-area ratios (FAR)** in urban areas. The floor-to-area ratio is also a very important term for the exam, and it is calculated by dividing the total square feet of a building by the total square feet of the lot of the building. For example 10,000 square feet of land that has a FAR of 2 can allow the construction of a 20,000-square-foot building. If the building has two stories, each story can contain 10,000 square feet of space, which in this case, the building would cover the whole lot since the lot also measures 10,000 square feet. (These types of building, which are built on the entire lot, are called **zero-lot-line projects**.)

Another 10,000 square feet of land that has a FAR of 1 would allow construction of a 10,000-square-foot building. Again, if the building has two stories, and each story contains 5,000 square feet of space, in which case the remaining 5,000 square feet of the lot could contain parking or landscape. Hence, a higher FAR allows more building space and a denser development.

PROTECTING THE HABITAT BY CHOOSING THE RIGHT LOCATION

To protect the habitat, green buildings should not be developed inside **sensitive lands**; instead, **infill sites** should be preferred. Infill sites, or infill developments, are sites that were either previously developed or were already being used for other purposes in urban areas. An example of an infill site could be a project location inside the downtown of a city that was used as a parking lot. Or it could be the site of a demolished building. Since infill sites have existing infrastructure and also have public transportation options, locating the project at an infill site would not create the negative consequences of suburban sprawl.

Going back to sensitive lands, below are the types of sensitive lands that should be avoided for development:
- Prime farmland
- Sites close to wetlands and water bodies (lakes, rivers, etc.)
- Public parkland
- Areas below floodplain
- Areas that are a part of the habitat or endangered species

Locating the project on **brownfield sites** and remediating them before the start of construction can be another option, which can also gain extra points in the LEED certification.

Brownfield sites are previously developed sites that were contaminated with waste or pollution. A site that has an abandoned building with unknown contamination can also be classified as a brownfield site. Once the contamination is cleaned up, these sites can be an excellent option for project development, and the federal, state, or municipal government can offer tax incentives on the property to support development.

Figure 3. A brownfield site (courtesy of Petr Vilgus)

TRANSPORTATION

Another key component of LEED is transportation, which accounts for 50% of a project's total greenhouse gas emissions and 33% of greenhouse gas emissions in the United States, according to the US Energy Information Administration.[2] The transportation sector is also responsible for about one-quarter of energy-related greenhouse gas emissions globally.[3]

A project should reduce the consequences of transportation by ensuring access to alternative modes of transportation to reduce single-occupancy vehicle use; encouraging walking and bicycling; and actively promoting alternative-fuel vehicles (such as green vehicles, that do not work by burning fossil fuels) by providing fueling facilities for green vehicles and/or reducing the parking rates for such vehicles. If the project is located in a high-density area or infill site, building occupants can walk to diverse uses and find different options for using public transit.

Project sites without access to public transportation can focus on local connectivity and may promote the use of green vehicles for commuting, provide incentives for carpooling, develop diverse uses that allow workers to walk to basic services, or facilitate the use of alternative-fuel vehicles such as plug-in hybrids.

Alternative-fuel vehicles do not rely on gasoline or diesel fuels and are instead powered by electricity, hydrogen, ethanol, natural gas, or biofuel. As this will be further discussed under the "Green Vehicles" credit, the cars that are eligible to be green vehicles can be classified under **Zero Emission Vehicles** by the **California Air Resources Board (CARB)** or should have earned a **Green Score of 45** or more from the **American Council for an Energy-Efficient Economy (ACEEE).**

Utilizing a **compressed workweek** can be another strategy to reduce fossil fuel usage. A compressed workweek typically occurs when a company allows its employees to work more hours during working days in exchange for a day off on a weekday. Alternatively, companies could utilize **telecommuting** for a part of the workweek so that employers could work from their homes without commuting to the office. Carpooling can also be rewarded, and parking rates could be made more expensive to discourage individual vehicle use.

LEED promotes minimizing the parking spaces inside buildings to the code minimums in order to discourage individual vehicle use, which will be further discussed under the "Reduced Parking Footprint" credit.

If the development location is close to a bicycle network, providing bicycle racks and shower rooms helps building occupants use their bicycles to commute and engage in daily physical activity.

NEIGHBORHOOD PATTERN AND DESIGN

To discourage suburban sprawl, we should pay special attention to the neighborhood pattern and design. A healthy neighborhood should contain wide sidewalks, benches, and bicycle networks. Business centers, retail services, educational facilities, and other diverse uses should be close enough to minimize travel. Public transportation options should be easily accessible. Street layouts should allow for easy connectivity, and if community gardens, farmers markets, and agricultural programs are established, a neighborhood could also be able to support access to sustainable food.

The aforementioned strategies are also a part of **compact development strategies,** which promote efficient neighborhoods and reduce greenhouse gas emissions.

STRATEGIES TO ADDRESS LOCATION AND TRANSPORTATION

- Promote smart growth
- Develop in dense areas
- Reuse or renovate an existing building or develop an infill site
- Protect habitat by avoiding development on sensitive lands
- Choose brownfields for project development by first remediating the whole site
- Locate near existing infrastructure
- Choose locations with diverse uses (examples of diverse uses would be banks, restaurants, schools, retail shops, and more.) Diverse uses should be within walking distance of the project location in order to promote walkability and reduce car dependency.
- Locate the project near public transit
- Limit the amount of parking spaces in the project
- Encourage walking by building occupants
- Promote bicycling by installing bicycle racks and shower rooms
- Encourage car-share programs
- Encourage carpooling and modify parking rates to discourage single-occupancy vehicle use
- Utilize a compressed workweek and/or telecommuting as much as possible
- Encourage green vehicle use by providing alternative fueling stations for green vehicles in the parking lot and allow for discounted parking rates
- Design walkable streets and pedestrian amenities such as benches, trees, and shade in general for neighborhood development
- Use compact development strategies for neighborhood development
- Promote connectivity in the neighborhood development
- Provide diverse land uses and diverse communities inside the neighborhood development
- Promote alternative transportation when developing neighborhoods
- Support access to sustainable food when developing neighborhoods
- Support access to grocery stores when developing neighborhoods

LOCATION AND TRANSPORTATION CREDITS

LEED FOR NEIGHBORHOOD DEVELOPMENT LOCATION—CREDIT

- 8–16 Points

CREDIT SUMMARY

The LEED for Neighborhood Development Location rating system is designed to provide smart growth and promote sustainability in neighborhoods. If a project is located inside one of those LEED ND-certified sites, the project will receive points under this credit.

The points will be awarded according to the located land's level of LEED ND certification (see table 2 for point distribution). For example, if the project is inside a LEED ND Platinum site, the project will get full points out of this credit.

Projects pursuing this credit will not be eligible to receive any other LT credits since a project located on LEED ND-certified land will mostly cover the goals of the other LT credits. This is also the reason why this credit contains lots of points. However, if the project teams see that they can earn more points in total from the other Location and Transportation credits, then the project teams should pursue those credits instead and avoid this credit.

CREDIT INTENT

The intent of this credit is to avoid development on inappropriate sites, to reduce vehicles miles traveled, and to contribute to human health by encouraging daily physical activity and enhancing livability.

CREDIT REQUIREMENTS

In order to be eligible for this credit, the project has to be inside a boundary of one of the following:

a. LEED ND Pilot—Stage 2 LEED for Neighborhood Development Certified Plan
b. LEED ND Pilot—Stage 3 LEED for Neighborhood Development Certified Project
c. LEED 2009—Stage 2 Precertified LEED for Neighborhood Development Plan
d. LEED 2009—Stage 3 LEED ND Certified Neighborhood Development
e. LEED v4—LEED for certified Neighborhood Development Certified Plan
f. LEED v4—LEED for certified Neighborhood Development Certified Built Project

If the project is under one of the sites below, no points will be awarded under this credit:

a. LEED ND Pilot—Stage 1 LEED for Neighborhood Development Prereviewed Plan
b. LEED 2009—Stage 1 Conditional Approval of LEED ND Plan
c. LEED v4—LEED for Neighborhood Development Conditional Approval

Basically, the LEED ND sites need to be "certified" in order to gain points under this credit. Conditional approvals or prereviewed LEED ND sites do not count.

	LEED ND Certified	LEED ND Silver	LEED ND Gold	LEED ND Platinum
BD+C	8 points	10 points	12 points	16 points
BD+C CS	8 points	12 points	16 points	20 points
BD+C Schools	8 points	10 points	12 points	15 points
BD+C Healthcare	5 points	6 points	7 points	9 points

Table 2. Points awarded for locating a project inside an LEED ND site

KEY THINGS TO REMEMBER

■ Projects pursuing this credit will not be eligible to receive any other LT credits, since a project located inside a LEED ND certified land will mostly cover the goals of the other LT credits.

■ LEED ND sites needs to be "certified" in order to gain points under this credit. Conditional approvals or pre-reviewed LEED ND sites do not count.

SENSITIVE LAND PROTECTION—CREDIT

- 1 Point

CREDIT SUMMARY

This credit is designed to prohibit site development in ecologically sensitive areas. Ecologically sensitive areas have a variety of benefits not only for human health but also for the environment. By locating the building's footprint on a previously developed area, ecologically sensitive areas are saved.

If the project is located on previously developed land, it will earn the credit because the land had already lost its ecological value. However, if the land, or <u>a portion of the land,</u> has not been previously developed, then any portion of the project should not be located on any sensitive areas—prime farmland, floodplain, habitat, water bodies, or wetland—in order to earn the credit.

CREDIT INTENT

The intent of this credit is avoiding the development of environmentally sensitive lands and reducing the ecological impact from the location of a building on a site.

CREDIT REQUIREMENTS

Option 1: 1 Point
Locate the development footprint on previously developed land.

OR

Option 2: 1 Point
If the land is not developed, then the land or a portion of the land should not fall under any of the categories below:

a. **Prime farmland**: This is defined by the **US Department of Agriculture**, United States Code of Federal Regulations Title 7, Volume 6, Parts 400 to 699, Section 657.5 and identified in a state Natural Resources Conservation Service (NCRS) soil survey. If the project is located outside the United States, then the project team can document a local equivalent, showing that the site is not prime farmland and can be used as an alternative compliance path (ACP).

b. **Floodplains:** This is defined by the floor hazard maps of the Federal Emergency Management Agency (FEMA) or local authorities. If no map exists, then the project teams will need to make sure the area is not subject to 1% or greater chance of flooding in any year. Qualified personnel can be hired to determine the chance of flooding on the land.

c. **Habitat:** This is land that hosts endangered or threatened species, according to the **US Endangered Species Act** or **NatureServe** data.

d. **Water bodies:** No development can be made within 100 feet (30 meters) of water bodies, except in the case of some minor improvements specified below.

e. **Wetlands:** No development can be made within 50 feet (15 meters) of wetlands except some minor improvements specified below.

Below are the minor developments that are acceptable <u>within</u> water bodies and wetlands. (All the minor developments must also be available to all building users.):

- Brownfield areas can be remediated.
- Grading can be made to allow for public access.
- Any activity to maintain or restore natural hydrology or native natural communities can be implemented.
- Pedestrian walkways or bicycle lanes can be constructed up to 12 feet wide (3.5 meters), and no more than 8 feet (2.5 meters) of that can be impervious.
- Trees that meet the following ratings can be removed:
  - Trees that are under 40% condition rating
  - Trees whose diameters are less than 6 inches (150 millimeters) at breast height
  - Hazardous trees
  - 75% of dead trees can be removed
  - Up to 20% of the trees whose diameters are less than 6 inches (150 millimeters) at breast height with a condition rating of 40% or higher

  Project teams must consult with an arborist certified by the International Society of Arboriculture (ISA) to verify the tree condition.
- Clearings that do not exceed 500 square feet (45 square meters)
- Only one single-story structure per 300 linear feet (90 linear meters)

If the project is outside the United States, local equivalents to the references above can be used. And for determining the sensitive habitat and endangered species, project teams may use the **International Union for Conservation of Nature Red List.**

KEY THINGS TO REMEMBER

- US Department of Agriculture, United States Code of Federal Regulations Title 7, Volume 6, Parts 400 to 699, Section 657.5—Defines the prime farmlands
- Federal Emergency Management Agency (FEMA)—Defines floodplains
- US Endangered Species Act—Defines endangered/threatened species
- NatureServe—Defines endangered/threatened species
- International Union for Conservation of Nature Red List Global list for endangered/threatened species

HIGH PRIORITY SITE—CREDIT

- 1–2 Points

CREDIT SUMMARY

Just like the "Sensitive Land Protection" credit, this credit also aims to preserve the greenfields and ecologically sensitive lands; however, in this instance the requirements are different. To encourage development on high priority areas, the credit requires a project to be developed either on an infill location inside a historic district, or inside one of the high-priority development areas determined by communities and governments, or in a brownfield site that needs to be remediated before use.

Locating the project inside a historic district will promote redevelopment of the historic district. Locating the project inside one of the high-priority development areas will promote the socially and economically depressed neighborhood. And locating the project in a brownfield will promote the recovery of a polluted site and provide lots of benefits to the environment.

CREDIT INTENT

To encourage the project location to be inside areas with development constraints and promote the health of the surrounding areas.

CREDIT REQUIREMENTS

Option 1: Historic District—1 Point
Locate the project on an infill location inside a historic district. **For a land to be qualified as an infill site, at least 75% of the land should be already developed within a half mile (800 meters) of the project boundary.**

OR

Option 2: Priority Designation—1 Point
Locate the site in one of the following priority development areas:
- A site listed by the EPA's National Priorities List
- A Federal Empowerment Zone site
- A Federal Enterprise Community site
- A Federal Renewal Community site

- A Department of the Treasury Community Development Financial Institutions Fund Qualified Low-Income Community (a subset of the New Markets Tax Credit Program)
- A site in US Department of Housing and Urban Development's Qualified Census Tracts (QCT) or Difficult Development Areas (DDA)
- A local equivalent program administered at the national level for projects outside the United States

OR

Option 3: Brownfield remediation—2 Points

Locate the project on a soil or groundwater contaminated brownfield that needs to be remediated according to the formal authorities guidelines.

KEY THINGS TO REMEMBER

- US Environmental Protection Agency (EPA)'s National Priorities List—Defines national priority sites.
- US Housing and Urban Development—Defines Federal Empowerment Zone, Federal Enterprise Community, and Federal Renewal Community
- US Department of Treasury, Community Development Financial Institutions Fund—Provides funds for low-income communities
- Names of the priority development areas

SURROUNDING DENSITY AND DIVERSE USES—CREDIT

- 1–5 Points

CREDIT SUMMARY

A project located inside existing built density and/or that is at a walkable distance to diverse uses such as banks, restaurants, supermarkets, etc. has great benefits to both the project users and to the environment, as it will also contribute to compact development. Increasing the residential and nonresidential densities in an area will reduce vehicle use and consequently reduce the air pollution as well, together with greenhouse gas emissions. Car accidents will also be less likely to occur.

In addition, this credit will award points for projects that are located inside surrounding densities and/or at a walking distance to the diverse uses. If the project satisfies both criteria, then the total points of both options will be awarded.

CREDIT INTENT

The intent of this credit is to conserve land and protect farmland and wildlife habitat by promoting development in areas with existing density. Promoting daily walks, improving transportation efficiency, and reducing vehicle distance traveled are part of the intent, as is improving human health by encouraging physical activity.

CREDIT REQUIREMENTS

Option 1: Surrounding density—2–3 Points

Locate the project on a site where the quarter mile (400-meter) radius of the project boundary meets the values in the table below. Use either "separate residential and nonresidential densities" or "combined density."

Combined density	Separate residential and non-residential Densities		Points
Sqft per acre of buildable land	Residential density (DU/acre)	Non-residential density (FAR)	
22,000	7	0.5	2
35,000	12	0.8	3

Table 3. Points awarded according to the location density

AND/OR

Option 2: Diverse Uses—1–2 Points

Locate the project so that the building's main entrance is within a **half mile** (800 meters) walking distance of the main entrance of four to seven (1 point) or eight or more (2 points) existing and available diverse uses shown on table 4.

Category of diverse use	Use type
Food retail	Supermarket
	Grocery
Community-serving retail	Convenience store
	Farmers market
	Pharmacy
	Hardware store
	Other retail
Services	Bank
	Family entertainment venue (theater)
	Gym, health club, exercise studio
	Laundry, dry cleaner
	Hair care
	Restaurant, cafe, diner
Civic and community facilities	Adult or senior care (licensed)
	Child care (licensed)
	Community or recreation center
	Cultural arts facility (museum, performing arts)
	Education facility (K-12 school, university)
	Education center, vocational school, community college
	Government office that serves public on-site
	Medical clinic or office that treats patients
	Place of worship
	Police or fire station
	Post Office
	Public library
	Public park
	Social services center
Community anchor uses	Commercial office (100 or more full-time equivalent jobs)

Table 4. Diverse uses

However, the same type of diverse use cannot be counted as more than two diverse uses. For example, if there are four restaurants at a walking distance, they can only be counted as two diverse uses. Additionally, facilities from at least three of the five diverse-use categories below should be present.

KEY THINGS TO REMEMBER

- Categories of diverse uses.
- In LEED, half mile (800 meters) is the walking distance to diverse uses that is measured from the main entrance of the building to the main entrance of the diverse use.

ACCESS TO QUALITY TRANSIT—CREDIT

- 1–5 Points

CREDIT SUMMARY

As with the previous credit, locating the project within walking distance of quality transit will reduce single-occupancy vehicle use, thereby reducing air pollution, including greenhouse gas emissions.

The environmental harms of public transport are known to be far less than that of single-occupancy vehicles. Additionally, access to quality public transit will be considerably helpful to people who do not own a car or to elderly people who can't drive.

CREDIT INTENT

Promote development in locations that have multimodal transportation choices, which reduces motor vehicle use and thereby reduces greenhouse gas emissions, other air pollution, and other environmental negatives associated with motor vehicles.

CREDIT REQUIREMENTS

Locate any functional entry of the building within a **quarter mile** (400 meters) walking distance of existing or planned bus, streetcar, or rideshare stops. Or locate the entry within a **half mile** (800 meters) walking distance of planned or existing bus rapid transit stops, light/heavy rail stations, commuter rail stations or commuter ferry terminals. Planned but currently non-operational stations can be counted if they're sited, funded, and under construction at the time of the certificate of occupancy and should be completed within twenty-four months from that date.

To earn the credit, the transit services must meet the values on table 5 and table 6:

Minimum daily transit service for multiple transit types (bus, streetcar, rail or ferry)		
Weekday Trips	Weekend Trips	Points
72	40	1
144	108	3
360	216	5

Table 5

Minimum daily transit service for commuter rail or ferry service only		
Weekday Trips	Weekend Trips	Points
24	6	1
40	8	2
60	12	3

Table 6

To earn the credit, both the required number of weekday and weekend trips should be met. The trips can be counted only in one direction, and if a qualifying transit has more than one stop at a walking distance, only one stop can be counted. If any of the transit types, located at a walking distance to the project, is temporarily rerouted (for less than two years), it can still be counted toward credit compliance.

KEY THINGS TO REMEMBER

- For all the LEED credits that require walking distance calculations, walkability should be confirmed by the use of paths that provide safe and comfortable environments for pedestrians and are part of a continuous network of sidewalks. Any walking route that does not fulfill these requirements cannot be documented as being within walking distance.
- In LEED, quarter mile (400 meters) is the walking distance to the bus, streetcar, or rideshare stops, and half mile (800 meters) is the walking distance to the bus rapid transit stops, light/heavy rail stations, commuter rail stations or commuter ferry terminals.

BICYCLE FACILITIES—CREDIT

- 1 Point

CREDIT SUMMARY

We all know the great benefits of bicycling for human health. Bicycling can translate to a lower risk of cardiovascular disease and other benefits that can extend human life. This credit is aimed at promoting a bicycle-friendly design in order to support the health of the building users and to reduce the emissions that would otherwise be generated by vehicle use.

To earn this credit, the projects will need to be located close to bicycle networks and contain bicycle storage and shower rooms. There should be both **long-term** and **short-term bicycle storage,** since the users and visitors will have different storage needs.

CREDIT INTENT

The intent of this credit is to promote the use of bicycles, transportation efficiency, reduction of vehicle distance traveled, and improvement of human health by promoting utilitarian and recreational physical activity.

CREDIT REQUIREMENTS

Bicycle network:

The project should be located so that the building's functional entry or bicycle storage is within **200 yards** (180 meters) of a bicycle network that connects to at least one of the following:

- At least 10 diverse uses (see table 4 in the "Surrounding Density and Diverse Uses" credit)
- An employment center or school, if the project's total area is 50% or more residential
- Light or heavy rail station, bus rapid transit stop, commuter rail station, or ferry terminal

All these diverse uses should be within a three-mile (4800 meters) bicycling distance of the project boundary. Planned but currently nonexisting bicycle networks can be counted, too, if they're funded by the date of the certificate of occupancy and rescheduled to be finished within a year of that date.

AND

Bicycle storage and shower rooms:

Case 1: Commercial or Institutional projects

Provide **short-term bicycle storage** (typically used by visitors for less than two hours, which is not an enclosed parking) for at least **2.5%** of all peak visitors (cannot be fewer than 4 spaces). And provide **long-term bicycle storage** (protected storage from rain and snow that is for residents and employees) for at least **5%** of all the regular building occupants (cannot be fewer than 4 spaces).

An on-site shower should also be provided with a changing facility for the first 100 regular building occupants and one additional shower for every additional 150 occupants.

Case 2: Residential projects

Provide short-term bicycle storage for at least **2.5%** of all peak visitors (cannot be less than 4 spaces). And provide long-term bicycle storage for at least **30%** of all the regular building occupants (cannot be less than one storage space per residential unit).

Case 3: Mixed-use projects

Meet case 1 and case 2 storage requirements for the residential and nonresidential portion of the project separately.

All the short-term bicycle storage should be within 100 feet (30 meters) of any main entrance. All the long-term bicycle storage should be within 100 feet (30 meters) of any functional entry.

In order to earn this credit, a project should satisfy both the bicycle network requirements and the bicycle storage and shower room requirements. Residential projects are exempt from the shower room requirement.

KEY THINGS TO REMEMBER

■ Definition of long-term bicycle storage and short-term bicycle storage.
■ For commercial and institutional projects, in addition to bicycle storage, on-site showers should be provided with a changing facility.

REDUCED PARKING FOOTPRINT—CREDIT

- 1 Point

CREDIT SUMMARY

Parking spaces create a considerable amount of harm to the environment. First, the surfaces of the parking lots trap heat (especially the dark-colored surfaces); this results in heat island effects, which increase the ambient air temperatures in urban areas. We have all seen that, in hot climates, asphalt parking lots release air just like a hair dryer blowing hot air. However, if a greenfield was there, this effect wouldn't occur.

In addition, because of the impervious surfaces of parking lots, rainwater runoffs will occur, which overwhelm the municipal stormwater systems and carry contaminants into the waterways. Again, if there was a greenfield instead of a parking lot, the soil would absorb all the rainwater without transferring it to the municipal stormwater systems. For those reasons, the aim of this credit is to reduce and limit the amount of parking spaces to the minimums.

To allow for further reducing the amount of the parking footprint, **transportation demand management strategies** can be implemented as well:

- Telecommuting
- Compressed workweek schedule
- Providing shuttles for employees
- Residential units sold separately from parking
- Shared parking between uses
- Transit subsidy

CREDIT INTENT

The intent of this credit is to minimize environmental harm related to automobiles, land consumption, rainwater runoff, and parking facilities.

CREDIT REQUIREMENTS

Projects should not exceed the minimum local code requirements for parking capacity.

Additionally, projects should provide parking capacity that is a percentage reduction below the base parking capacity ratios of the **Parking Consultants Council, as shown in the Institute of Transportation Engineers' Transportation Planning Handbook, 3rd edition, Tables 18-2 through 18-4.**

Case 1: Baseline location

Projects that have not earned points under "Surrounding Density and Diverse Uses" or "Access to Quality Transit" credits should achieve a 20% reduction from the base parking capacity ratios.

Case 2: Dense and/or transit-served location

Projects that have earned 1 or more points under either the "Surrounding Density and Diverse Uses" credit or "Access to Quality Transit" credit should achieve a 40% reduction from the base parking capacity ratios.

For all projects

The calculations must also include all the out-of-the-project-boundary parking spaces that are leased or owned by the project. Public on-street parking is exempt from the calculations. For projects that use pooled parking, the project's share in the pooled parking should be calculated.

Projects also need to provide preferred parking for carpools for 5% of the total parking after the reductions have been made from the base ratios. If there isn't any off-street parking, then preferred parking is not required.

Mixed-use projects should determine the percentage reduction by calculating the parking amount of each use specified by the base ratios. Parking spaces for fleet and inventory vehicles are exempt from these calculations unless the vehicles are regularly used by employees for commuting.

KEY THINGS TO REMEMBER

- Base parking capacity ratios are referenced from the Parking Consultants Council, as shown in the Institute of Transportation Engineers' Transportation Planning Handbook, 3rd edition, Tables 18-2 through 18-4.
- Transportation demand-management strategies.

GREEN VEHICLES—CREDIT

- 1 Point

CREDIT SUMMARY

This credit promotes the use of green vehicles (vehicles that score a minimum of 45 points on the **American Council for an Energy-Efficient Economy (ACEEE)** annual vehicle rating guide) by providing exceptions for them, including preferred parking spaces, discounted parking rates, and **electric vehicle charging stations, also known as EVSE (electric vehicle supply equipment).**

In the United States, transportation accounts for 27% of the total greenhouse gas emissions from combustion of petroleum-based fuels.[4] The use of petroleum-based fuels is a serious cause of climate change and is the main source of air pollution.

Figure 4. Electronic vehicle charging station (EVSE) (courtesy of Michiel Bonbenal)

CREDIT INTENT

The intent of this credit is to reduce pollution by encouraging alternatives to conventionally fueled automobiles.

CREDIT REQUIREMENTS

Projects should designate **5%** of all the parking spaces as preferred parking for sole use by green vehicles. Preferred parking spaces should be distributed proportionally among various parking sections. Required signage should be posted on the preferred parking locations to show that those preferred locations are reserved for green vehicles.

As an alternative to providing preferred parking to green vehicles, a discounted parking rate of at least **20%** for green vehicles can be provided. The discounted rate must be publicly posted at the entrance of the parking area and should be available to every green vehicle permanently.

To be considered a green vehicle, a vehicle must achieve a minimum green score of **45** on the **American Council for an Energy-Efficient Economy (ACEEE)** annual vehicle rating guide (or the equivalent for projects outside the United States).

In addition to preferred parking/discounted parking for green vehicles, project teams should meet one of the following two options:

Option 1: Electric vehicle charging—1 point
Install **electric vehicle supply equipment (EVSE)** in 2% of all the parking spaces. Reserve and identify these spaces for sole use by the plug-in electric vehicles. Parking spaces with EVSE must be provided separately and in addition to the preferred parking spaces reserved for green vehicles. The EVSE should:
- Provide Level 2 charging capacity (208–240 volts) or greater
- Comply with the relevant regional or local standard for electrical connectors
- Be networked or accessible from the internet and be capable of participating in a demand-response program (demand response will be discussed in depth under the "Demand Response" credit)

OR

Option 2: Liquid, gas, or battery facilities—1 point
Install liquid or gas **alternative fuel*** fueling facilities or a battery switching station capable of refueling a number of vehicles per day equal to at least 2% of the total parking spaces.

* Alternative fuels are the nongasoline, low-polluting fuels like <u>hydrogen</u>, <u>electricity</u>, <u>propane</u>, <u>compressed natural gas</u>, <u>liquid natural gas</u>, <u>methanol</u>, and <u>ethanol</u>.

KEY THINGS TO REMEMBER

- Green vehicles must achieve a minimum green score of 45 on the American Council for an Energy-Efficient Economy (ACEEE) annual vehicle rating guide.
- Names of alternative fuels.

DOCUMENTING LT CREDITS

To demonstrate achievement of a credit under the LT credit category, necessary documentation and calculations should be prepared with the following considerations:

Calculations for walking and bicycling distances:

Walking and bicycling distances are measurements to demonstrate how far a pedestrian and bicyclist would travel to a destination, such as the nearest grocery store.

The walking distance, also called the **shortest path analysis**, must be measured along infrastructure that is safe and comfortable for pedestrians (such as sidewalks and crosswalks). And cycling distances must be measured along infrastructure that is safe and comfortable for cyclists (such as bicycle lanes, off-street bicycle paths, etc.)

When calculating these distances for both walking and bicycling, the sum of the continuous segments of the route will give the total distance from the origin to the destination. A straight-line radius that does not follow safe pedestrian and bicyclist infrastructure will not be accepted.

Calculations for total vehicle parking capacity:

The following parking spaces must be included in total parking capacity:

- New and existing surface parking spaces
- New and existing garage or multilevel parking spaces
- Any off-street parking spaces outside the project boundary that serve the building's users

The following parking spaces should not be included in total parking capacity:

- Public on-street parking spaces
- Parking spaces assigned to fleet and inventory vehicles (unless these vehicles are used by employees for commuting as well as business purposes)
- Motorbike or bicycle spaces

If there is a shared parking space among two or more buildings (which is also called pooled parking), then the project's share in the parking should be included in the calculations.

If there isn't any parking space assigned to the project, the project will be awarded the "Reduced Parking Footprint" credit; however, such a situation would not merit the award of the "Green Vehicles" credit.

Calculations for preferred parking:

Preferred parking spaces should have the shortest walking distance to the main entrance of the project (exclusive of spaces designated for people with disabilities).

If parking is provided in a multilevel facility, the preferred spaces should be located on the level that is closest to the main entrance of the building. If there are different parking areas for different kinds of building users (customer parking, staff parking, etc.), then a project can distribute the required preferred parking spaces proportionally across each different type of parking area. The same logic also applies to the fueling stations in the "Green Vehicles" credit.

CHAPTER 6

SUSTAINABLE SITES (SS)

This chapter will discuss both the importance of sustainable sites and their effects on the green building design. After discussing the SS credit category, the book will go over all the SS prerequisites and credits individually to show how these features are used in LEED certification for a LEED BD+C: New Construction and Major Renovation project.

The Sustainable Sites credit category will be discussed under six major sections:

- Site assessment
- Site design
- Minimizing construction impacts
- Rainwater management
- Heat island effect
- Site management

SITE ASSESSMENT

As an important aspect of the integrated process of creating a sustainable site, a site assessment first needs to be conducted in order to have the relevant information that will be necessary for the site design.

The project team can conduct an assessment evaluating the following site features:

- **Topography:** Contour mapping, slope stability risks, unique topographic features
- **Hydrology:** Floor hazard areas, delineated wetlands, lakes, streams, shorelines, rainwater collection, and reuse
- **Climate:** Solar exposure, seasonal sun angles, winds, precipitation values
- **Vegetation:** Primary vegetation types, significant tree mapping, threatened or endangered species, habitat
- **Soils:** Prime farmland, healthy soils
- **Human use:** Views, proximity to transportation, proximity to diverse uses, adjacent properties
- **Human health effects:** The degree of air pollution on-site, the level of contamination present on-site, proximity to vulnerable populations

SITE DESIGN

With the completion of the site assessment, the project team will have the necessary information to proceed with the site design. When designing the site, all the development footprint of the project should be considered as a whole. (A **building footprint** is the area that the building sits on, and the **development footprint** is the sum of all the areas that are affected by the project's activity in the project site. Thus, the development footprint will cover the building footprint and the sidewalks, access roads, hardscapes, parking lots, etc.).

Many people enjoy spending time with pristine views and natural surroundings. In light of this, when designing a development footprint, the project team should always think about preserving open spaces, which will allow the occupants to spend time in the outdoors in a picturesque landscape. In addition, if there are any damaged areas on the project site, including damaged existing vegetation, the project team can work on restoring them to support the environment. Employing these strategies will benefit the environment and society while increasing the project value.

Choosing the type of vegetation to be used in the project is an important decision that will greatly impact outdoor water use consumption. If the project chooses to use **native** or **adapted plants**, they will need less irrigation and maintenance, which will reduce the water use of the project since those plants are accustomed to naturally surviving in that climate.

Native plants (or indigenous plants) are the type of plants that occur and develop naturally in a specific location. Adapted plants are the types of plants that do not occur naturally in a specific location; however, they can nonetheless adapt easily to the climate of the region. In summary, both native and adapted plants can thrive without extensive irrigation, pesticides, and fertilizers.

Other types of plants will require more maintenance and consume more irrigation water, which will result in increased maintenance costs. Plants can be selected to minimize **evapotranspiration**, which is the term used for the return of water to the atmosphere through evaporation from plants. In dry climates, projects can use plants with low evapotranspiration rates, which would require less irrigation water compared with plants with higher evapotranspiration rates.

Invasive plants that exist on-site should be cleared from the site, otherwise they will take over the adjacent existing native and adapted plants. Invasive plants are the types of plants that spread and damage the environment.

Lighting is another important factor that needs to be addressed during the site design. During the green building design, all types of light pollution should be avoided. There are two types of lighting pollution. The first type is the annoying light that intrudes on an otherwise natural or low-light setting, and the second type is the excessive light that leads to discomfort and adverse health effects.

During the lighting design, the project team should eliminate uplighting, glare, overlighting and light trespass (light spilling out of the project boundary) in order to conserve energy and to not create discomfort in the adjacent properties. Direct full cutoff fixtures should point downward to illuminate the project site. The use of shield fixtures will aid in avoiding light trespass and the spilling of light beyond the project boundary.

Innovative approaches can also be discovered for more efficient lighting. An example of this could be the use of **reflective paving materials**, which would help distribute the light across the site; as a result, the number of fixtures needed to illuminate the area would be reduced, as would the building operating costs. For areas that need more lighting, timers can shut off the lighting late at night.

As will be discussed under the "Light Pollution Reduction" credit, LEED started to request the use of the **backlight-uplight-glare (BUG)** rating method to show compliance with sustainable lighting measures as well as the standards of the **Illuminating Engineering Society of North America (IESNA)**, which sets lighting specifications for building design. To summarize, for a LEED certification, the careful selection and placement of lighting fixtures is needed during the site design phase.

Further, there are other factors to consider when designing a sustainable site, which will be discussed under the "Rainwater Management" and "Heat Island Effect" credits.

MINIMIZING CONSTRUCTION IMPACTS

The environmental impacts of construction activities should be minimized, and the necessary strategies should be evaluated before the start of construction.

While grading the project site, the project team should take measures to prevent erosion and sedimentation. To limit erosion and sedimentation, the following methods can be considered:

- Mulching
- Sediment (silt) fencing
- Erosion control blankets
- Berms and constructed ponds
- Seeding
- Straw bales

Sediment fences can be installed around the project site to prevent soil runoff and excessive erosion. The topsoil should always be protected in order to avoid erosion in sloping areas. Projects close to wetlands and water bodies should take extra precautions, and make sure the sensitive areas are not affected by construction activities. Taking constructive action will have a positive effect on local water quality and avoid damage to the infrastructure of the city.

In order to protect the neighborhood, necessary precautions should be taken to prevent dust caused by construction activities from polluting the neighborhood. Those precautions might include cleaning the trucks and other construction vehicles serving the project before leaving the site.

RAINWATER MANAGEMENT

Most people have probably seen the gigantic pipes of storm sewers, which are responsible for carrying stormwater to avoid flooding. But what is the reason that municipalities are working so hard to get rid of this much water?

Think about an undeveloped piece of land with a ground surface of soil. In this scenario, there wouldn't be any flooding. Moreover, rainwater would not be considered as an enemy, but would rather be a best friend.

After we started developing the world, soil was replaced by impervious surfaces, through which the rainwater cannot be absorbed by the soil. Now, all the rainwater that falls on impervious surfaces add up to vast amounts of water that need to be transferred somewhere else. In turn, the transferal of such amounts of rainwater results in other consequences.

With the stormwater runoff, water gets contaminated by harmful chemicals and then flows into natural bodies of water such as seas, oceans, or lakes, resulting in a degraded surface water quality, which consequently harms aquatic life and prevents recreational opportunities.

This type of pollution is also called **nonpoint source pollution** since the point of the pollution source cannot be identified.

Because the rainwater can't be absorbed and filtered by the soil, it cannot replenish the aquifers. To summarize, the natural hydrology of the ecosystem cannot work anymore, and green buildings need to address rainwater management to protect the environment.

The first goal of a green building for rainwater management should be for it to contain the least number of impervious surfaces. Furthermore, the rainwater that falls onto the pervious surfaces should be collected and retained (this is called **on-site water retention**), or at least its flow should be slowed down. If the flow of the rainwater cannot be slowed down, heavy rainfall will overwhelm result in the overwhelming of the municipal storm sewer system.

To minimize impervious surface areas, projects can use vegetated roofs, rain gardens, porous pavements, grid pavers, and additional landscaping in order to allow rainwater absorption through the soil. In parking lots, pervious paving or open-grid paving can be used instead of using asphalt or concrete. For LEED, an impervious surface is a surface that contains less than **50%** perviousness.

Figure 5. Vegetated roofs (courtesy of Erik Christensen)

Rainwater harvesting, another aspect of rainwater management, is a process whereby rainwater is collected and filtered to be reused as an alternative to potable water. The filtered rainwater can be used for irrigation, for toilet and urinal flashing, or even for process water in cooling towers. For storing the filtered rainwater, installing cisterns will be necessary.

Another efficient rainwater management strategy is the use of **low-impact development (LID),** which is an approach to mimic natural systems and to manage the stormwater closest to its source. LID strategies include decreasing impervious surfaces and increasing vegetation on-site. LID is used to slow down the flow of rainwater out of site and ensures that the rainwater does not get contaminated.

Some strategies of LID include:

- Use of **dry ponds** (detention ponds), which hold the excess rainwater for some time, thereby allowing the rainwater to slowly seep into the ground without contamination. (Dry ponds are excavated areas that detain and slow down stormwater but are dry at other times.)
- Use of **bioswales** and **vegetated filters,** which filter water by having it run through vegetation or through rocks. (Bioswales are a stormwater-control feature that uses a combination of engineered basin, soils, and vegetation.)
- Bioretention

Green infrastructure (GI) technologies are accepted in LEED for managing the rainwater as well. Green infrastructure is known to direct the rainwater, collected from impervious surfaces, to vegetation and soil surfaces without routing it to the storm sewer system.

Figure 6. Dry pond (detention pond) (courtesy of Michelle Dorothy)

HEAT ISLAND EFFECT

An example of heat island effect would be the black asphalt surfaces radiating heat on a hot summer day, with the air rising from the asphalt like hot air from a hair dryer. If there was a grass or soil area instead of a black-colored asphalt, as it would have existed before the development, this effect would not occur, as soil cannot absorb the solar heat like black colored asphalt does.

Disturbing the environment with dark-colored, nonreflective surfaces causes the heat island effect. These surfaces absorb heat during hot weather and release it into the atmosphere. Studies show that urban "heat islands" are responsible for 24.2% of global warming.[1] And because of this effect, urban areas can have air temperatures that are 1.8° F to 22° F warmer than the surrounding suburban areas. Higher temperatures will also lead to smog or ground level ozone, which creates consequences for human health.

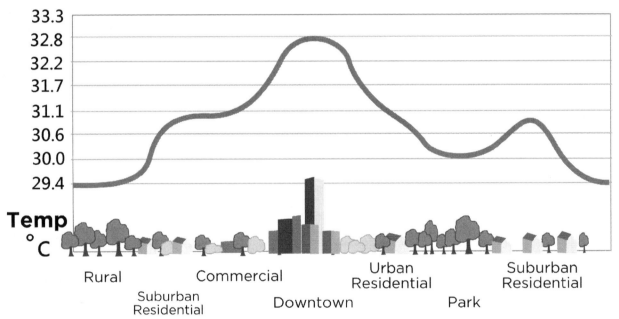

Figure 7. Urban heat island profile (courtesy of National Oceanic and Atmospheric Administration)

Heat islands are also responsible for increased cooling loads in buildings, which result in higher electricity usage and harm to plants and animals that are sensitive to temperature changes.

Think about wearing a black T-shirt on a hot summer day when walking under the sun at noon, and compare the difference of heat that will be absorbed by the black T-shirt with a white T-shirt.

The black T-shirt will absorb all the heat from the sun while the white T-shirt will reflect back the heat. This can be explained by the differences of their **solar reflectance (SR)** and **solar reflectance index (SRI)** values.

A solar reflectance (SR) value will show the solar energy that is reflected by a surface on a scale of 0 to 1. A black surface will have an SR of 0 while a white surface will have an SR of 1.

A material's SRI value will indicate a material's ability to stay cool by reflecting solar radiation and emitting thermal radiation. Thus, both the solar reflectance and **emissivity** of a material will be combined to rank the material. Emissivity (infrared or thermal emittance) is a measure that shows how much heat or infrared radiation a material can shed back into the atmosphere. The SRI value of a material is measured from a scale of 0 to 100, and, within that scale, light-colored materials are closer to scoring a 100 SRI while darker-colored materials are closer to scoring 0 SRI. (Lighter-colored materials are sometimes called high **albedo** materials, which is another type of reflectivity measurement.) **Thus, the higher the SRI or SR, the lower the heat island effect.**

In order to classify building materials according to their solar emissions and reflectance, the **solar reflectance index (SRI)** will be used for the <u>roofing materials,</u> and **solar reflectance (SR)** values will be used for the <u>nonroof materials</u> (such as hardscape) in LEED credit calculations. And in addition to the initial SR and SRI values, <u>three-year-aged SR</u> and <u>SRI</u> values will also be needed for LEED credit calculations since the materials' performance will drop as they age.

Below are some strategies to reduce heat island effects:

- Minimize the development footprint (Less development will mean more soil surface.)
- Undercover/underground parking
- Using hardscape materials with high SR values
- Reducing the area of paved surfaces exposed to sunlight
- Installing vegetated roofs (Green roofs are much durable than regular roofs and have great acoustical and insulation qualities.)
- Installing **cool roofs** (roofs that reflect more sunlight and absorb less heat compared with traditional dark-colored roofs)
- Using roof surfaces with high SRI values (lighter-colored roofs)
- Providing shade from trees, structures covered by solar panels, or architectural devices with high SR values
- Using solar panels on the roof
- Using open-grid paving (In LEED open-grid pavement should be at least 50% permeable.)
- Using **cool pavements** (pavements that reflect more sunlight and absorb less heat compared with traditional pavements)

Figure 8. Open-grid pavement (courtesy of Immanuel Giel)

However, in colder climates, using roofing materials with a lower SRI value can benefit the project by decreasing the heating costs since the roof will be able to absorb more heat from the sun.

SITE MANAGEMENT

Careful plant selection, innovative irrigation systems, and an efficient outdoor lighting design are some strategies that will aid in sustainable site management. During the site management phase, strategies below can be implemented:

- Utilize **Integrated Pest Management (IPM)**, which is known as a sustainable approach that combines knowledge about pests, nature, pest prevention, and control methods that minimize pest infestation and damage while minimizing hazards to the building occupants, the property itself, and the environment. Measures should always be taken to first prevent the attraction of pests. Using native and adapted plants for the landscaping can be an effective strategy to combat pests
- Develop a sustainable site management plan
- Implement conservation programs with ecologists and nonprofit organizations to protect wildlife species and habitats
- Use nontoxic chemicals for cleaning outside the building

- Use nontoxic snow- and ice-removal products
- Carefully use fertilizers and maintenance products in landscaping
- In accordance with the Royal Astronomical Society of Canada's light-abatement recommendations, all site lighting should be fully cut off and designed to eliminate nighttime light pollution, while preserving the integrity of the night sky

STRATEGIES TO ADDRESS SUSTAINABLE SITES

- Protect and restore habitat
- Minimize construction impacts
- Conduct a site assessment to assess and evaluate topography, hydrology, climate, vegetation, soils, human use, human health effects
- Preserve open space
- Use native landscaping (by using native and adapted plants)
- Minimize hardscape
- Minimize the development footprint
- Minimize impervious areas; maximize pervious areas
- Incorporate stormwater management into the site design
- Control and redirect stormwater (by installing dry ponds, rain gardens, bioswales, etc.)
- Utilize low-impact development (LID) and green infrastructure (GI)
- Harvest rainwater
- Eliminate uplighting, glare, overlighting, and light trespass
- Maintain site lighting to prevent light pollution
- Reduce the heat island effect
- Install reflective roof surfaces
- Provide undercover/underground parking
- Reduce the area of paved surfaces exposed to sunlight
- Plant an urban forest or a green roof
- Use products with high SR and SRI values
- Develop a sustainable site management plan
- Implement conservation programs
- Use nontoxic chemicals for site cleaning
- Implement Integrated Pest Management (IPM)

SUSTAINABLE SITES PREREQUISITES AND CREDITS

CONSTRUCTION ACTIVITY POLLUTION PREVENTION—PREREQUISITE

PREREQUISITE SUMMARY

In most parts of the world, there are codes to ensure that all construction projects implement an Erosion and Sedimentation Control (ESC) plan, which protects the environment and the neighborhood from the pollution created by construction activities. This prerequisite ensures, even if there is not a local code, that the project disturbances to the neighboring properties, to the site, and to the rainwater systems are minimized.

The prerequisite forces projects to establish an ESC plan according to the erosion and sedimentation requirements of the **2012 US Environmental Protection Agency (EPA) Construction General Permit (CGP)** or local equivalent, whichever is more stringent.

The following are some of the issues to be addressed:

- The slope of the project site and where water will drain
- The total area and duration of ground disturbance to identify air quality and rainwater runoff effects on neighboring properties
- The location of existing rainwater management systems that must be protected
- Weather and soil conditions that can create rainwater runoff or generate dust
- Construction entrances and their effects on local roads servicing the project site

PREREQUISITE INTENT

The intent of this prerequisite is to reduce the pollution created from construction activities by controlling soil erosion, airborne dust, and waterway sedimentation.

PREREQUISITE REQUIREMENTS

Create and implement an erosion and sedimentation control (ESC) plan for all construction activities associated with the project.

The plan must conform to the erosion and sedimentation requirements of the 2012 US Environmental Protection Agency (EPA) Construction General Permit (CGP) or a local equivalent, whichever is more stringent. Projects must apply CGP regardless of their size.

The plan should also describe the measures implemented.

KEY THINGS TO REMEMBER

■ In LEED, the ESC plan needs to conform to the erosion and sedimentation requirements of the 2012 US Environmental Protection Agency (EPA) Construction General Permit (CGP).

SITE ASSESSMENT—CREDIT

- 1 Point

CREDIT SUMMARY

Site assessment is a part of the integrative process, which clearly shows the project teams the properties of the site, including its topography, hydrology, climate, soil types, water availability, and human health effects. By conducting a site assessment, the project team can orient the building to take advantage of the solar access, or can decide which types of plants would be well suited to the site conditions for landscaping. Please remember that the building orientation has the greatest effect on the building's energy consumption.

CREDIT INTENT

Before the design, assess the site conditions to evaluate suitable options and to inform related decision-making about the site design.

CREDIT REQUIREMENTS

Prepare and document a site survey or assessment that includes the following:
- **Topography:** Contour mapping, slope stability risks, and unique topographic features
- **Hydrology:** Flood hazard areas, lakes, delineated wetlands, streams, shorelines, rainwater collection and reuse opportunities, and TR-55 initial water storage capacity of the site (or local equivalent for projects outside the United States)
- **Climate:** The site's solar exposure, heat island effect potential, seasonal sun angles, prevailing winds, monthly precipitation, and temperature ranges
- **Vegetation:** The site's primary vegetation types, significant tree mapping, threatened or endangered species, unique habitat, greenfield area, and invasive plant species
- **Soils:** Natural Resources Conservation Service soils delineation (a soil survey showing all the different types of soil on-site), US Department of Agriculture prime farmland, healthy soils, disturbed soils, and previous development
- **Human use:** Views, the site's transportation infrastructure, adjacent properties, and construction materials with existing recycle or reuse potential
- **Human health effects:** Proximity of vulnerable populations, adjacent physical activity opportunities, and proximity to major sources of air pollution

The assessment should document how the project design was influenced. If any of the mentioned topics are not addressed by the project team, then an explanation should be provided.

KEY THINGS TO REMEMBER

- A site assessment includes evaluation of topography, hydrology, climate, vegetation, soils, human use, and human health effects.

SITE DEVELOPMENT—PROTECT OR RESTORE HABITAT—CREDIT

- 1–2 Points

CREDIT SUMMARY

This credit is aimed to both protect the on-site greenfield during construction and restore damaged habitat. The project teams should protect at least 40% of their greenfield on-site during the construction. (To qualify as a greenfield, that area should have not been previously developed, graded, or disturbed.) Moreover, the projects should restore at least 30% of the previously disturbed land by revegetation—or, instead, provide financial support to a nationally or locally recognized land trust or conservation organization.

CREDIT INTENT

The intent of this credit is to promote conservation of existing ecological areas and restoration of contaminated areas, to provide habitat and promote biodiversity.

CREDIT REQUIREMENTS

Preserve and protect 40% of the greenfield area on the site, if it exists, from all development and construction activity.

AND

Option 1: On-site restoration—2 Points
By using native or adapted vegetation, restore 30% (including the building footprint) of all portions of the site that were previously disturbed. Projects that achieve a density of 1.5 floor-to-area ratio may also include vegetated roof surfaces in this calculation if native and adapted plants are used.

    Restore all disturbed soils that will be revegetated to meet the following requirements:

      ➤ Soils must be reused for functions similar to their original function

❧ Imported topsoils or soil blends designed to serve as topsoil cannot include either of the following:

- Soils defined regionally by the **Natural Resources Conservation Service Web Soil Survey** as prime farmland, unique farmland, or farmland of statewide or local importance.
- Soils from other greenfield sites, unless those soils are a byproduct of a construction process.

❧ Restored soil should meet the criteria of **reference soils** (reference soils are the native soils of a site) in categories 1, 2, and 3 and meet the criteria of either category 4 or 5:

1) Organic matter
2) Compaction
3) Infiltration rates
4) Soil biological function
5) Soil chemical characteristics

Vegetated landscape areas that are constructed to accommodate rainwater infiltration from the vegetation and soils requirements are exempt from this calculation.

OR

Option 2: Financial support—1 point

Provide financial support equivalent to at least $0.40 per square foot ($4 per square meter) for the total site area, including the building footprint. Financial support must be provided to a land trust or conservation organization within the same **EPA Level III ecoregion** or the project's state, or within 100 miles (160 km) of the project for projects outside the United States. For projects located in the United States, the land trust must be accredited by the **Land Trust Alliance,** which is an organization that provides accreditation to land trust organizations.

KEY THINGS TO REMEMBER

■ Natural Resources Conservation Service Web Soil Survey defines soils as prime farmland, unique farmland, or farmland of statewide or local importance.

■ Land Trust Alliance.

OPEN SPACE—CREDIT

- 1 Point

CREDIT SUMMARY

We all love to go to the parks, lie on the grass, and spend time with our friends or read books. We also know that open spaces provide great health benefits to individuals. This credit encourages projects to provide outdoor spaces that are <u>accessible to all building users</u>, and which also <u>contain vegetation</u>.

CREDIT INTENT

The intent of this credit is to provide an exterior open space that would promote interaction with the environment, passive recreation, social interaction, and physical activities.

CREDIT REQUIREMENTS

Provide outdoor space more than or equal to 30% of the total site area (including the building footprint). A minimum 25% of the provided outdoor space must be vegetated (turf grass does not count as vegetation) or have overhead vegetated canopy.

The outdoor space must be physically accessible and be one or more of the following:

- Pedestrian-oriented paving or turf area with physical site elements that accommodate outdoor social activities for building occupants
- Recreation-oriented paving or turf area with physical site elements that encourage physical activity for building occupants
- Garden space with different vegetation types and species that provide opportunities for year-round visual interest
- Garden space dedicated to community gardens or urban food production
- Preserved or created habitat that meets the criteria of the "Site Development—Protect or Restore Habitat credit", which also includes elements of human interaction

For projects that achieve a density of 1.5 floor-area ratio (FAR), **extensive** or **intensive vegetated roofs** can also be used. The vegetated roof should meet the minimum 25% vegetation requirement, and the roof's physically accessible paving areas can be used toward credit compliance.

Extensive vegetated roofs are the types of roofs that do not include a variety of plants, and they require little maintenance. Their soil layer is thinner compared with the intensive roofs since they're more designed for smaller-sized vegetation. Intensive vegetated roofs have a wider variety of plants and also have more soil depth to support those plants.

Wetlands or naturally designed ponds can also be counted as open space. But their side slope gradients should average 1:4 (vertical: horizontal) or less and need to be vegetated.

KEY THINGS TO REMEMBER

- Definitions of intensive and extensive vegetated roofs.
- In LEED, an open space area should be a minimum of 30% of the total site area, and a minimum of 25% of the open space must be vegetated. And open spaces should be accessible to all building users.

RAINWATER MANAGEMENT—CREDIT

- 2–3 Points

CREDIT SUMMARY

Before buildings were constructed, ground soils were able to absorb rainwater, and the rainwater was distributed in a natural way. With the development of construction projects, the natural hydrology of ecosystems was disturbed. The rainwater collected on impervious surfaces is now redirected to other areas, which have begun to receive too much water. At the same time, the soils under the impervious surfaces are not receiving any rainwater at all.

This particular credit aims to re-create the rainwater balance by promoting green infrastructure (GI) and low-impact development (LID) rainwater management strategies, which can be done by mimicking a site's natural hydrology, thus minimizing the disruption caused by the project.

To earn the credit, the total volume of rainwater runoff will be calculated according to the rainfall data of the project's location, and strategies will be implemented to manage the amount of rainwater.

CREDIT INTENT

The intent of this credit is reducing the rain-water runoff volume and improving water quality by replicating natural hydrology and water balance of the project site based on past climate data.

CREDIT REQUIREMENTS

Option 1: Percentile of rainfall events—2–3 Points

Path 1: 95th percentile—2 points
Manage on-site the runoff from the developed site for the 95th percentile of regional or local rainfall events by using green infrastructure and low-impact development (LID).

Use daily rainfall data as well as the methodology in the US Environmental Protection Agency (EPA)'s "Technical Guidance on Implementing the Stormwater Runoff Requirements for Federal Projects under Section 438 of the Energy Independence and Security Act" for determining the 95th percentile amount.

OR

Path 2: 98th percentile—3 points
>   Achieve Path 1 but, in this instance, for the 98th percentile of regional or local rainfall events, again using LID and green infrastructure.

OR

Path 3: Zero-lot-line projects only—85th Percentile—3 points
>   For the zero-lot-line projects in urban areas with a minimum density of 1.5 FAR, runoff from the developed site for the 85th percentile of regional or local rainfall events should be managed by using LID and green infrastructure. (Zero-lot-line projects are the projects in which their project boundary exactly aligns with the building footprint; in other words, the building sits on the whole project site.)

OR

Option 2: Natural land cover conditions—3 points
Under this option, project teams should manage the annual increase in on-site runoff volume, from the natural land cover condition to the post-developed condition.

In other words, the project teams need to find the natural land condition of the project site and then make a calculation to find how much rainwater it was able to absorb. Then the project teams should calculate how much rainwater the land can absorb under post-development conditions. The difference between those two values will give the extra runoff volume that occurs because of the project's disturbance to the site. That runoff volume needs to be managed in order to earn the credit under option 2.

KEY THINGS TO REMEMBER

- Green infrastructure (GI) and low-impact development (LID).
- Definition of zero-lot-line.

HEAT ISLAND REDUCTION—CREDIT

- 1–2 Points

CREDIT SUMMARY

Some examples of materials in a building that would be responsible for the heat island effect would be a dark-colored roof, dark-colored pavements, or asphalt surfaces. This credit awards points for minimizing a project's heat island effect by using vegetated roofs, light-colored non-roof measures, or high-reflectance roofs, or by providing covered parking. For the material-reflectance calculations, solar reflectance index (SRI) values will be used for roofs, and solar reflectance (SR) values will be used for nonroof measures.

CREDIT INTENT

Reducing the heat islands to minimize the effects on microclimates, wildlife habitats, and humans.

CREDIT REQUIREMENTS

Option 1: Nonroof and roof—2 points
Meet the following formula:

$$\frac{\text{Area of Non-roof Measures}}{0.5} + \frac{\text{Area of High-Reflectance Roof}}{0.75} + \frac{\text{Area of Vegetated Roof}}{0.75} \geq \text{Total Site Paving Area} + \text{Total Roof Area}$$

Use any combination of the following strategies.

For the <u>nonroof measures</u> on-site:
- Use the existing plants or install new plants that will provide shade over the paved areas on the site within 10 years of planting. Install vegetated planters. Plants must be in place at the time of the occupancy permit, and artificial turf cannot be included.
- Provide shade with structures covered by energy generation systems (e.g., solar thermal collectors, photovoltaics, wind turbines, etc.)

- Provide shade with architectural devices or structures that have a three-year aged solar reflectance (SR) value of at least 0.28. If the information is not available, use materials with an initial SR of at least 0.33.
- Provide shade with vegetated structures.
- Use paving materials with a three-year aged solar reflectance (SR) value of at least 0.28. If the information is not available, then use materials with an initial SR of at least 0.33.
- Use an open-grid pavement system with at least 50% unbound.

For high-reflectance roof:

Use roofing materials that have an SRI equal to or greater than the values in the following table. Meet the three-year aged SRI value as well. If the three-year aged SRI value is not available, use materials that meet the initial SRI value.

	Minimum solar reflectance index value by roof slope		
	Slope	Initial SRI	Three-year aged SRI
Low-sloped roof	≤ 2:12	82	64
Steep-sloped roof	> 2:12	39	32

Table 7

Projects can also install a <u>vegetated roof</u> in order to satisfy the formula.

OR

Option 2: Parking under cover—1 point

Place at least 75% of parking spaces under cover. Any roof that is used to shade or cover parking must meet one of these three qualifications:

- Have a three-year aged SRI of at least 32 (If a three-year aged SRI value is not available, use materials with an initial SRI of at least 39.)
- Be a vegetated roof
- Be covered by energy-generation systems, such as solar thermal collectors, photovoltaics, or wind turbines

Figure 9. Undercover parking with PV panels (courtesy of Tatmouss)

KEY THINGS TO REMEMBER

■ For the heat island effect calculations, SR, SRI, and also three-year aged SR and three-year aged SRI values are used in LEED.

■ For nonroof measures, SR values are used; for roofs, SRI values are used.

■ The use of lighter-colored surfaces reduces the heat island effect, and higher SR and SRI means lower heat island effect.

LIGHT POLLUTION REDUCTION—CREDIT

- 1 Point

CREDIT SUMMARY

Light pollution is another factor that creates environmental problems. Overexposure to artificial lighting causes sleeping problems in humans, disorientation for birds, and light pollution is a waste of energy that can bring further environmental impacts.

This credit requires projects to establish efficient lighting designs, and in order to establish an efficient lighting design, a project should reduce the <u>uplight</u>, <u>glare,</u> and <u>light</u> <u>trespass</u>. Backlight is the primary factor of light trespass onto adjacent sites, uplight is the cause of artificial glow, and glare is caused by high-angle front lights.

The **BUG rating method** is also used in the credit; the method is a luminaire classification system that classifies a luminaire according to backlight, uplight, and glare.

CREDIT INTENT

This intent of this credit is to improve nighttime visibility and night sky access and reduce the consequences of development for wildlife and people.

CREDIT REQUIREMENTS

Meet uplight and light trespass requirements by using either the backlight-uplight-glare (BUG) method in option 1 or the calculation method in option 2. Different options for uplight and light trespass can be used as well.

The uplight, light trespass, and glare requirements should be met for all the exterior luminaires based on the <u>photometric characteristics</u> of each luminaire and the <u>lighting zone</u> of the project. The lightings that are exempt from these requirements are:
- Lighting for theatrical purposes, stages, etc.
- Directional lightings in transportation
- Road marking lightings
- Roadway lightings
- Hospital emergency department and helipad lightings
- National flag lightings
- Internally illuminated signage (This has its own requirement in the following pages.)

For Uplight:

Option 1: BUG rating method
Based on the specific light source installed in the luminaire, the following luminaire uplight ratings below, as defined in IES TM-15-11, Addendum A, should not be exceeded.

Maximum uplight ratings for luminaires	
MLO lighting zone	Luminaire uplight rating
LZ0	U0
LZ1	U1
LZ2	U2
LZ3	U3
LZ4	U4

Table 8

OR

Option 2: Calculation method
Do not exceed the percentages below for total lumens emitted above horizontal.

Maximum % of total lumens emitted above horizontal by lighting zones	
MLO lighting zone	Maximum allowed % of total luminaire lumens emitted above horizontal
LZ0	0%
LZ1	0%
LZ2	1.5%
LZ3	3%
LZ4	6%

Table 9

AND

For Light trespass:

Option 1: BUG rating method
Do not exceed the following luminaire backlight and glare ratings as defined in IES TM-15-11, Addendum A, based on the mounting location and distance from the lighting

boundary. The **lighting boundary** is located at the property lines of the project. Following are some conditions that can modify the lighting boundary of the project:

- If the property line is adjacent to a public area that is a parking lot, walkway, bikeway, or plaza, the lighting boundary can be moved 5 feet beyond the property line
- If the adjacent properties are also owned by the same entity
- When a property line is adjacent to a street, alley, or transit corridor, the lighting boundary can be moved to the centerline of the street, alley, or transit corridor.

Option 2: Calculation method
Do not exceed the required vertical illuminance levels at the lighting boundary.

AND

<u>For internally illuminated exterior signage</u>: Do not exceed 200 cd/m^2 (nits) luminance at night and 2000 cd/m^2 (nits) during the day.

KEY THINGS TO REMEMBER

- Backlight is the primary factor of light trespass onto adjacent sites, uplight is the cause of artificial glow, and glare is caused by high-angle front lights.
- The items that are exempt from uplight, glare, and trespass requirements.
- The lighting boundary is located at the property lines of the project.
- The definition of the BUG rating method.

CHAPTER 7

WATER EFFICIENCY (WE)

Seventy percent of the earth's surface is covered by water; however, fresh water only comprises 1% of the total volume and is the only percentage that is accessible for human use. According to the United Nations Environment Programme, if the current water consumption rates continue, two out of every three people will live in water-stressed conditions by the year 2025.

With the increase of residential, commercial, and industrial development, the use of potable water increases. From flushing toilets to industrial water uses, potable water is becoming wastewater, which overwhelms treatment facilities and results in heavy energy use during water treatment, as well as creation of more greenhouse gases.

Green buildings need to address this issue by improving their water efficiency. Please note that "efficiency" does not mean finding an alternative method; rather, it means doing the same thing by using less of the same resource. As a result, water will still be used, but it will be used in a smarter way.

The **water balance** approach, which aims to balance water supply with water consumption, is not achievable for every location.

(An example of the water balance approach would be to use only captured rainwater and/or underground water for the water needs of the building, so no water would be used from municipal lines.) Nonetheless, getting as close as possible can still bring about a considerable change.

This chapter will discuss both the importance of water efficiency and its effect on the green building design. After discussing the WE credit category, the book will go over all the WE prerequisites and credits individually to show how these features are used in LEED certification for a LEED BD+C: New Construction and Major Renovation project.

The WE credit category will be discussed under two major sections:

- Indoor water use
- Outdoor water use

However, before getting into the finer details, the required LEED calculations for both indoor and outdoor water use need to be mentioned. This information will be also used in the WE prerequisites and credits.

LEED INDOOR AND OUTDOOR WATER USE CALCULATIONS

For indoor water use: When approaching the strategies to reduce the water consumption of a project, it is necessary to first calculate a **baseline** water usage and then find innovative ways to establish water use reductions from the baseline during the design phase. In LEED, projects will be awarded points under the WE credits according to the percent reduction made from their baseline water usage.

To calculate the baseline water usage of a project, first the baseline rates for flow and flush fixtures and fittings should be determined. In the LEED prerequisite and credit calculations, the baseline flow and flush rates are specified by the **Energy Policy Act of 1992 (EPAct 1992)**.

The occupant usage should then be calculated to find out how much those fixtures and fittings will be used. This calculation is made to demonstrate that the more occupants there and the more time they spent in a building, translate to greater total water usage.

In LEED, the **Full-time equivalent (FTE)** value will be used to determine the occupant usage of the fixtures and fittings. And to obtain the FTE of the building, the occupants will first be identified by the following occupant types:

- Full-time staff
- Part-time staff
- Transient occupants (who do not use the facility consistently, such as visitors, customers, students, etc.)
- Residents

The number of FTE occupants is based on a standard 8-hour occupancy period. A full-time staff member who works 8 hours a day will have an FTE of 1, while a part-time staff member who works 4 hours a day will have an FTE of 0.5. FTE calculations will also include multiple shifts.

In a building that contains 40 full-time occupants and 20 part-time occupants, the total FTE for only the full-time and part-time staff would be:

$$(40 \times 1) + (20 \times 0.5) = \mathbf{50}$$

In addition, the FTE values of transient occupants and residents also need to be calculated and added to the "50" in order to calculate the total FTE of the building.

Once the FTE is calculated and the baseline flow and flush rates for fixtures and fittings are taken from the Energy Policy Act of 1992 (EPAct 1992), the baseline indoor water consumption can be calculated. Next, project teams will need to discover innovative strategies for reducing water consumption as much as possible.

For outdoor water use: The projects that contain landscaping will need to calculate the baseline **landscape water requirement (LWR)**. LWR is the amount of water that the landscape will require during the site's peak watering month.

To calculate the LWR, projects will use the **US Environmental Protection Agency (EPA)'s WaterSense Water Budget Tool**. This is an online calculating tool which the project team needs to input the types of vegetation, the area of each vegetation, project location, and irrigation system type. With this information, the online tool will calculate the total LWR of the project, which will be the baseline value. Next, project teams will need to discover innovative ways for reducing this value.

Projects without a landscape will be exempt from outdoor water use calculations.

INDOOR WATER USE

Use of water for urinals, toilets, showers, kitchen, and other applications all contribute to indoor water use. Indoor potable water consumption can be reduced by using water-efficient fixtures and fittings and/or using nonpotable water sources where appropriate.

The use of **WaterSense**-labeled products can be a good strategy that will contribute to reducing indoor water usage. WaterSense is a program developed by the US Environmental Protection Agency to identify high-performance, water-efficient fixtures and fittings. A fixture or a fitting that has a WaterSense label will guarantee high water efficiency.

Following are different types of efficient fixtures and fittings that can be installed to decrease potable water consumption:

- ➤ Dual-flush toilets: This type of toilets have two buttons, one for full flush, the other one for half flush, depending on the type of waste.
- ➤ High-efficiency toilets (HETs): WaterSense-labeled toilets, which save 20% of the water typically used in every flush.
- ➤ Waterless urinals: These types of urinals do not need any water and have lower maintenance costs.
- ➤ Composting toilet systems: Such systems do not require any water since they treat waste with a microbiological process.
- ➤ Low-flow showerheads and faucets
- ➤ Faucets with low-flow aerators and/or motion sensors

In addition to high-efficiency fixtures, the use of harvested **rainwater** and/or **graywater** as the flush water of toilets can decrease potable water consumption.

Graywater is the untreated household water that does not come into contact with toilet waste. Used water from bathtubs, showers, bathroom washbasins, and clothes washers and laundry tubs can be examples of graywater and may be used as flush water in toilets or urinals.

By installing graywater treatment systems, the used water can be filtered and then sent back to the building for reuse. <u>The definition of graywater changes from state to state, and some states do not allow the use of graywater as toilet flush water</u>. Because of this, it is advised that the project team first check with the local code requirements before deciding on using graywater.

It is also important to mention **blackwater** and **reclaimed water** for the purposes of the exam. Blackwater is the term to describe the used water that has come into contact with waste. Thus, the water collected from the urinals and toilets can be classified as blackwater. Reclaimed water is former blackwater that has been treated and purified for reuse and can even be used for irrigation. However, projects again need to be verified according to local code requirements, as some codes may classify some types of reclaimed water as blackwater and may not allow its use.

Reducing **process water** usage is also essential in reducing potable water usage. Process water is the type of water used by mechanical or other types of systems in buildings such as cooling towers or medical equipment in hospitals. Using reclaimed water, harvested rainwater, or graywater as process water can make a great contribution to reducing potable water consumption. If the projects also choose to install **closed-loop** systems, which use and circulate the same process water inside, instead of using **open-loop** systems, then even more potable water can be saved. Open-loop systems require outside water (which is called the **makeup water**) to support the system.

Installing submeters would be another plus for the projects to track and log water use trends and check fixture performance. Further, it would allow for the discovery of innovative ways to reduce potable water usage.

Without any such data, it wouldn't be possible to identify individual water use of the building systems and pinpoint the items that consume high amounts of potable water.

When doing water-use calculations for LEED, the water usage of **flush fixtures** such as toilets and urinals is measured in **gallons per flush (gpf)**. For **flow fixtures**, such as sink faucets, showerheads, and aerators, the water usage is measured in **gallons per minute (gpm)**.

OUTDOOR WATER USE

In some projects, potable water used for irrigation exceeds the total indoor water consumption of the building. Water reductions in irrigation can be established through water-wise landscaping designs, water-efficient irrigation technologies, nonpotable water use (such as using reclaimed water, graywater, or harvested rainwater), and installation of submeters to track and log irrigation trends.

As mentioned before, careful plant selection will make a great contribution to reducing outdoor water use. The use of native and adapted plants, or **xeriscaping** (type of landscaping that does not need any irrigation), and clearing out any invasive plants can help considerably. Areas covered with turf or grass will need high amounts of irrigation water. Project teams should evaluate the related LEED prerequisites and credits before deciding on their use. **Mulching** around a plant, which is a protective layer applied to the surface of soil, will help to keep the roots of the plants cool and therefore prevent evaporation.

Using high-performance irrigation technologies such as **drip irrigation systems, bubbler distribution systems**, and **channel water directly to root systems** are other strategies to consider. The use of **weather-based irrigation controllers**, to respond to weather conditions, will avoid watering the vegetation while it is raining.

Drip irrigation systems are the types of microirrigation systems that drip water to the roots of plants to minimize the use of irrigation water and fertilizers. They are the <u>most water-efficient systems</u> and have very short payback periods. Scheduling of the irrigation is important, as it is best to water the landscape in the early morning, which is the coolest part of the day.

For the projects that install a landscape that does not require any permanent irrigation, the period after the first two years of the new planting will be considered in the LEED prerequisites and credits, as the newly planted landscape will need more water to become established in the first two years.

Figure 10. Xeriscape demonstration garden in Denver Water HQ, Denver Colorado (courtesy of Jeffrey Beall)

STRATEGIES TO ADDRESS WATER EFFICIENCY

- Install efficient plumbing fixtures such as dual-flush toilets, high-efficiency toilets (HET), waterless urinals, composting toilet systems, low-flow showerheads and faucets, and faucets with low-flow aerators and/or motion sensors
- Use nonpotable water such as reclaimed water, harvested rainwater, and graywater as indoor water
- Install submeters to individually track indoor water consumption
- Use native or adapted plants and avoid invasive plants
- Use xeriscaping
- Install high-efficiency irrigation systems such as drip irrigation systems, bubbler distribution systems, and systems that channel water directly to root systems with weather-based irrigation controllers
- Use nonpotable water such as reclaimed water, harvested rainwater, and graywater as outdoor water
- Install submeters to track and log outdoor water consumption

WATER EFFICIENCY PREREQUISITES AND CREDITS

OUTDOOR WATER USE REDUCTION—PREREQUISITE

PREREQUISITE SUMMARY

Water is our main resource for living, and it should not be used at a faster rate than it can be replenished. Unfortunately, in some cities, the water levels are rapidly decreasing, which is likely to cause many serious problems in the future.

In nonagricultural water use, landscape irrigation can use 30% to 70% of water consumed. This prerequisite forces the smart use of outdoor water by choosing landscaping that requires no irrigation (xeriscaping), or the project will need to reduce its landscape irrigation water requirement (LWR) by a minimum of **30%** from the calculated baseline. Projects without any landscapes will be exempt from this prerequisite.

PREREQUISITE INTENT

To reduce outdoor water consumption.

PREREQUISITE REQUIREMENTS

Option 1: No irrigation required
As the name implies, if a project contain a landscape that does not need any irrigation beyond a maximum of a two-year establishment period, documenting it will fulfill the prerequisite.

OR

Option 2: Reduced irrigation
Reduce the project's landscape water consumption by at least **30%** from the calculated baseline for the <u>site's peak watering month</u>.

This reduction should be established by selection of the plant species and irrigation systems according to their efficiency. For the landscape water requirement calculation, the EPA's WaterSense Water Budget Tool will be used.

Please remember that if a project has large areas of turf or grass, it will be harder to satisfy the prerequisite since their water consumption will be much higher than other vegetation types. Projects should mainly use native and adapted plants and avoid invasive plants. Nonvegetated areas should be excluded from these calculations. Athletic fields and vegetated playgrounds may be included or excluded from these calculations according to the project team's decision.

KEY THINGS TO REMEMBER

- The US Environmental Protection Agency's (EPA) WaterSense Water Budget Tool should be used for outdoor water use calculations.
- LEED requires all projects to reduce the baseline outdoor water usage **30%** from the calculated baseline for the site's peak watering month.
- How xeriscaping is used in LEED.
- How native plants/adapted plants/invasive plants are used in LEED.
- Athletic fields and vegetated playgrounds may be included or excluded from LEED outdoor water use calculations according to the project team's decision.

INDOOR WATER USE REDUCTION—PREREQUISITE

PREREQUISITE SUMMARY

This prerequisite aims to reduce indoor potable water usage by forcing the use of water-efficient fixtures and fittings. Project teams will need to calculate indoor water consumption and reduce the water usage **20%** by utilizing more efficient fixtures and fittings. The baseline calculations for determining indoor potable water usage will be according to the flush or flow rates in table 10, and calculating the FTE value of the project will be essential to figuring out the indoor potable water usage.

Furthermore, projects should use WaterSense-labeled products for all the newly installed toilets, urinals, private lavatory faucets, and showerheads that are eligible for WaterSense labeling.

If all the installed fixtures and fittings do not exceed WaterSense maximum levels, projects can earn the prerequisite by only documenting their fixtures' and applicable appliances' "**product cutsheets**" or "**fixture schedules**". And in this instance there will be no need to calculate the indoor water consumption of the building if the project does not intend to pursue the credit of this prerequisite: the "Indoor Water Use Reduction" credit.

The mentioned credit awards points for further reducing the indoor water consumption; however, to calculate the established percentage of water reduction, projects need to also calculate the indoor water consumption in this prerequisite since using solely WaterSense-labeled products will not be sufficient.

Appliances and process equipments are also addressed separately inside this credit, which can consume more water than all the other water-consuming items in the building.

PREREQUISITE INTENT

The intent of this prerequisite is to reduce indoor water consumption.

PREREQUISITE REQUIREMENTS

Building water use:
For the fixtures and fittings shown below, reduce aggregate water consumption by 20% from their baseline units.

For all newly installed toilets, urinals, private lavatory faucets, and showerheads (that are eligible), use WaterSense-labeled products or their equivalents for projects that are located outside the United States.

Fixture or Fitting	Baseline Water Consumption Values (IP units)
Toilet (water closet)	1.6 gpf
Urinal	1.0 gpf
Public lavatory faucet	0.5 gpm are 60 psi
Private lavatory faucet	2.2 gpm at 60 psi
Kitchen faucet	2.2 gpm at 60 psi
Showerhead	2.5 gpm at 80 psi

Table 10

Appliance and Process Water Use:

All appliances and processes must meet the following standards:

Appliance	Requirement
Residential clothes washer	ENERGY STAR or performance equivalent
Commercial clothes washer	CEE Tier 3A
Residential dishwasher	ENERGY STAR or performance equivalent
Prerinse spray values	Less than 1.3 gpm
Ice machine	ENERGY STAR or performance equivalent and use air-cooled or closed-loop cooling

Table 11

Process	Requirement
Heat rejection and cooling	No once-through cooling
Cooling towers and evaporative coolers	Must contain makeup water meters, conductivity controllers and overflow alarms, and efficient drift eliminators

Table 12

Please note that the baseline water consumption of the toilets and urinals are specified in gallons per flush (gpf) while others are specified in gallons per minute (gpm).

KEY THINGS TO REMEMBER

■ A toilet's baseline water consumption is 1.6 gpf; a urinal's baseline water consumption is 1.0 gpf.

■ In the LEED prerequisite and credit calculations, the baseline flow and flush rates are specified by the **Energy Policy Act of 1992 (EPAct 1992)**.

■ LEED requires all projects to reduce the baseline indoor water usage **20%** by utilizing more efficient fixtures and fittings and with the use of WaterSense-labeled products.

■ Note the items that fall under appliances, processes, or fixture/fittings. (It is possible to get a question asking if an ice machine falls under appliances or processes.)

■ If all the installed fixtures and fittings do not exceed WaterSense maximum levels, projects can earn the prerequisite only by documenting their fixtures' and applicable appliances' **"product cutsheets"** or **"fixture schedules."**

BUILDING LEVEL WATER METERING—PREREQUISITE

PREREQUISITE SUMMARY

With this prerequisite, USGBC aims to compare every project's designed water usage data with the actual water usage data, by tracking potable water use with the installation of water meters to all the potable water sources. All projects should commit to sharing their potable water data for five years, starting from the occupancy phase or LEED certification, whichever comes first.

Since disparities can occur between the designs of buildings and their actual performances, USGBC will collect and analyze data in order to identify the common traits among high and low performers and will also share its findings with the project teams so that they can improve their performance.

PREREQUISITE INTENT

The intent of this credit is supporting the project's water management and identifying opportunities for additional water savings by tracking water consumption.

PREREQUISITE REQUIREMENTS

Install permanent water meters that can measure the total potable water use for the building and associated grounds. Metered data should be collected in monthly and annual summaries. For a five-year period, whole-project water use data should be shared with USGBC starting on the date that the project accepts LEED certification or typical occupancy, whichever comes first.

KEY THINGS TO REMEMBER

- Why USGBC collects potable water usage data: USGBC will collect and analyze data in order to identify common traits among high and low performers and will also share its findings with the project teams so that they can improve their performance.
- For a five-year period, the whole-project water use data should be shared with USGBC starting on the date that the project accepts LEED certification or typical occupancy, whichever comes first.
- Metered data should be collected in monthly and annual summaries.

OUTDOOR WATER USE REDUCTION—CREDIT

- 1–2 Points

CREDIT SUMMARY

This is the credit of the "Outdoor Water Use Reduction" prerequisite and awards points for further reductions in outdoor water use.

In the prerequisite, the projects need to reduce their irrigation water by 30% from the calculated baseline for the site's peak watering month. And in this credit, projects will be awarded points if they can make a 50% or 100% reduction from the baseline. Alternative water sources (such as graywater) can also be used to make a reduction in the potable water beyond a certain threshold.

If the project has a landscape that does not need any irrigation beyond the two-year establishment period, then the credit will be automatically earned by the project.

CREDIT INTENT

The intent of this credit is reducing outdoor water consumption.

CREDIT REQUIREMENTS

Reduce outdoor water consumption through one of the following options.

Option 1: No irrigation required—2 points

Option 2: Reduced irrigation—2 points
Reduce the project's landscape water consumption by at least **50%** from the calculated baseline for the site's peak watering month. This reduction should be established by careful selection of the plant species and increasing the efficiency of the irrigation systems. The **US Environmental Protection Agency (EPA)'s WaterSense Water Budget Tool** will be used for water budget calculations.

Additional reductions beyond the prerequisite level (30%) may be achieved with the use of any combination of efficiency, alternative water sources, and smart scheduling technologies.

Nonvegetated surfaces such as pavements are excluded from landscape calculations. Athletic fields, vegetated playgrounds, and food gardens may be included or excluded from these calculations, according to the project team's decision.

% of water reduction from the baseline	Points
50%	1
100%	2

Table 13

KEY THINGS TO REMEMBER

- Potable water reduction can be established by careful selection of the plant species and increasing the efficiency of the irrigation systems.
- Alternative water sources include reclaimed wastewater, graywater, captured rainwater, swimming pool backwash water, ice machine condensate, municipally supplied treated wastewater, refrigeration system condensate, foundation drain, stormwater, and fluid cooler discharge.
- The US Environmental Protection Agency (EPA)'s WaterSense Water Budget Tool is used for water budget calculations.

INDOOR WATER USE REDUCTION—CREDIT

- 1–6 Points

CREDIT SUMMARY

This is the credit of the "Indoor Water Use Reduction" prerequisite, which aims for further indoor water use reduction.

In the prerequisite, the projects have to reduce their building water use by 20% from the calculated baseline, and in this credit, projects will be awarded points if they can make further reductions from the same baseline. Alternative water sources can be used to reduce potable water use. Those alternative sources include on-site surface sources, subsurface natural freshwater sources, graywater, on-site reclaimed water, collected rainwater, captured condensate, and nonpotable water from other than public utilities.

CREDIT INTENT

To reduce indoor water consumption.

CREDIT REQUIREMENTS

Further reduce the indoor water consumption from the calculated baseline in the "Indoor Water Use Reduction" prerequisite. Additional water savings above the prerequisite level (20%) can be established by using alternative water sources. Points will be awarded according to the level of water use reduction:

% of water reduction from the baseline	Points
25%	1
30%	2
35%	3
40%	4
45%	5
50%	6

Table 14

AND

Appliances and process water equipment should meet ENERGY STAR requirements.

KEY THINGS TO REMEMBER

- Alternative water sources can include on-site surface sources, subsurface natural freshwater sources, graywater, on-site reclaimed water, collected rainwater, captured condensate, and nonpotable water from other than public utilities.
- Appliances and process water equipment should meet ENERGY STAR requirements.

COOLING TOWER WATER USE REDUCTION—CREDIT

- ▪ 1–2 Points

CREDIT SUMMARY

This credit aims to reduce the water usage of cooling towers and evaporative condensers. When cooling the building, the HVAC system needs to take away heat from the building, and cooling towers are needed to release this heat into the atmosphere.

In order to release a building's heat into the atmosphere, cooling towers evaporate water using the building's heat. As the cooling tower water evaporates, the remaining water becomes more concentrated and starts to deposit scale, thereby reducing the cooling tower's efficiency. To minimize the deposit of scales, some of the cooling tower's water is replaced by fresh potable water. (The removal of water is called **blowdown.**) And **makeup water** is used to replace both the lost water from evaporation and the blowdown.

This credit chemically analyzes cooling tower water (condenser water) to evaluate its concentration levels and calculate how many cycles the cooling tower can make using the same condenser water without going beyond the targeted concentration levels in the credit.

To gain an additional point, projects can use a minimum of 20% of recycled nonpotable water in their cooling towers or can instead increase the cooling tower cycles beyond 10 by increasing the level of treatment in the condenser or makeup water.

CREDIT INTENT

Reducing the water used for cooling tower makeup while controlling corrosion, microbes, and scale in the condenser water system.

CREDIT REQUIREMENTS

For cooling towers and evaporative condensers, make a one-time potable water analysis and find the actual values of the parameters on table 15.

Find the number of cooling tower cycles by dividing the maximum allowed concentration level of each parameter by the actual concentration levels of each parameter found after testing. And limit the cooling tower cycles to avoid exceeding the maximum values for any of these parameters.

Parameter	Maximum Level
Ca	1000 ppm
Total alkalinity	1000 ppm
SiO2	100 ppm
CI	250ppm
Conductivity	2000 MS/cm

Table 15

Cooling tower cycles	Points
Maximum number of cycles achieved without exceeding maximum values (up to 10 cycles max)	1 point
Achieve a minimum of 10 cycles by increasing the level of treatment in the condenser or makeup water or meet the minimum number of cycles and use a minimum 20% recycled non potable water	2 points

Table 16

KEY THINGS TO REMEMBER

- Recycled nonpotable water can be used in cooling towers to reduce potable water usage.
- The purpose of makeup water.
- Definition of blowdown and why it is needed.

WATER METERING—CREDIT

- 1 Point

CREDIT SUMMARY

This is the credit of the "Building Level Water Metering" prerequisite, which forces the projects to track the water use of different subsystems. By submetering different building systems, a facility manager can then identify major water uses and look for ways to reduce water use.

CREDIT INTENT

To promote water management and evaluate opportunities for additional water savings by tracking water consumption.

CREDIT REQUIREMENTS

Install permanent water meters for at least two or more of the following water subsystems:
- Irrigation (for at least 80% of the irrigated landscape area)
- Indoor plumbing fixtures and fittings (for at least 80% of the fixtures and fittings)
- Domestic hot water (for at least 80%)
- Boiler (with an annual water use of more than 100,000 gallons)
- Reclaimed water
- Other process water (for at least 80%)

KEY THINGS TO REMEMBER

- The names of the six subsystems mentioned, which LEED requires to meter for advanced metering

CHAPTER 8

ENERGY AND ATMOSPHERE (EA)

This credit category contains the highest total points among the credit categories in LEED (33 points) because energy use and the burning of fossil fuels are the biggest contributors to global warming. Green buildings need to use less energy and preferably use energy from sustainable energy sources.

Similar to the water-efficiency credit category, in which the projects calculate baseline water usage and establish reductions by employing water-efficient strategies, in this credit category, the baseline energy usage of the whole building will be calculated, allowing the discovery of innovative ways to reduce building energy usage.

According to the study of the New Buildings Institute, LEED-certified projects use 24% less energy than regular buildings. Almost half of the green buildings in the study achieved an **ENERGY STAR Portfolio Manager**™ score of 75 or above, with an overall average score of 68.[1] The ENERGY STAR Portfolio Manager is an interactive, online management tool that enables the tracking and assessment of energy and water consumption. It was set up by EPA as a part of the ENERGY STAR program. With the ENERGY STAR Portfolio Manager, a score of 50 represents an average building performance.

In addition to the Portfolio Manager, there is another program called **ENERGY STAR TargetFinder**™, which allows projects to set target goals for a building design's energy demands. And according to their changes in the design, project teams can see the savings in energy demand. However, with TargetFinder, projects cannot compare their design performance with the actual energy usage, as they can do this with the Portfolio Manager.

The New Buildings Institute study also found that a significant percentage of buildings underperformed their benchmarks. This is why commissioning building systems and monitoring their performance is very important to ensure that the set benchmarks turn into actual performances.

This chapter will discuss both the importance of the Energy and Atmosphere credit category and its effect on green building design. After discussing the EA credit category, the book will go over all the EA prerequisites and credits individually to show how these features are used in LEED certification for a LEED BD+C: New Construction and Major Renovation project.

The EA credit category will be discussed under five major sections:

- Energy demand
- Use of refrigerants
- Energy efficiency
- Renewable energy
- Ongoing performance

ENERGY DEMAND

Green building projects need to set goals for saving energy. For the LEED certification, projects will gain points according to their percentage energy reductions from their baseline energy usage by trying different design alternatives and products. This will take place under the "Optimize Energy Performance" credit, which contains 18 total points and is the credit that contains the highest number of points.

Below are some strategies that can result in reducing the energy demand of buildings:

- **Building orientation** has the biggest effect on energy demand. By maximizing the southern exposure to the sun, buildings can have increased daylight and passive solar heating. (An example may be to orient the building in order to locate most of the windows facing south.) By minimizing western exposure, annual cooling costs can be dramatically reduced.
- **Community planning** can support building configurations in order to minimize solar gain in summer and maximize it in the winter.
- **Adjacent buildings** can be helpful in providing shade or insulation, or in blocking winds.

- **Passive strategies** like daylighting, thermal mass, and natural ventilation can reduce the energy demand for lighting, heating, and cooling.

- **Efficient building insulation** can reduce energy use.

- **Educating occupants** on their patterns of energy consumption can reduce energy demand.

- **3D computer modeling**, particularly when combined with building information modeling (BIM) software on energy design, can help a lot in evaluating different design alternatives by showing their outcomes. In addition, they can show the best locations for placing windows, doors, and other items.

- In existing buildings, conducting an **energy audit** can highlight the building systems that are not operating efficiently. **Home Energy Saver**™ can also be used to conduct a do-it-yourself energy audit, which is developed by the US Department of Energy to enable existing buildings to analyze, reduce, and manage their energy use.

- **Rightsizing** is another factor that will affect energy demand. The bigger the building, the higher the energy demand; therefore, projects should not be developed larger than their needs. In the LEED for Homes rating system, points are adjusted in all the categories according to the square footage of the home, which is called **home size adjustment (HSA)**. Thus, homes that are bigger need to earn more points to achieve a LEED certification while smaller-sized homes can become LEED-certified by earning fewer points. Other LEED rating systems do not have this size adjustment.

USE OF REFRIGERANTS

As well as reducing energy consumption, green buildings need to address the types of **refrigerants** used in the project. Refrigerants are the substances mostly used in air conditioning and refrigeration systems, and refrigerants will probably be the most important topic in the exam.

Refrigerants in building systems deplete stratospheric ozone, which is a gas that protects human health and the environment by absorbing harmful ultraviolet (UV) radiation. The depletion of ozone also contributes to climate change. The 1987 **Montreal Protocol** banned the production of **chlorofluorocarbon (CFC)** refrigerants, and it is also phasing out **hydrochlorofluorocarbon (HCFC)** refrigerants. The phasing out of CFCs in developed countries began in 1991. In the United States, the phasing out of CFCs was completed in 1995. And by 2030, less active HCFCs will be completely phased out.

The destructive potential of these chemicals is measured by both their ozone depletion potential (ODP) and global warming potential (GWP). Both CFCs and HCFCs are known to have ozone-depleting potential.

As will be discussed under the "Fundamental Refrigerant Management" prerequisite, LEED BD+C projects aiming for a LEED certification cannot use any CFC refrigerants, and existing buildings should complete a total CFC phase-out (clear completely) prior to project completion.

The **natural refrigerants** are much more environmentally friendly than the others, which are carbon dioxide (CO_2), water (H_2O), ammonia (NH_3), air, and hydrocarbons such as propane, ethane, and butane. A natural refrigerant's ODP and GWP values are zero or very close to zero; however, they are less effective than the HCFCs. For example, cooling a building with a natural refrigerant results in more energy consumption than with an HCFC refrigerant.

The discussion of refrigerants will continue under the "Enhanced Refrigerant Management" credit.

ENERGY EFFICIENCY

After reducing energy demand, the project team should look for ways to improve energy efficiency, which will result in doing the same amount of work with less energy.

ENERGY EFFICIENCY FOR HVAC SYSTEMS

With the integrated process, the project teams can employ synergic strategies. An example of a synergic strategy may be to install a building envelope that can result in installing a smaller HVAC system because of the high level of insulation provided by the envelope.

In 2005, the US Department of Energy estimated that 40% of the energy used to heat and cool the average building was lost to air leaks in the building envelopes. Building envelope problems can lead to high operating costs, uneven building temperatures, poor indoor air quality, building deterioration, noise, and other effects.

When choosing HVAC equipment, a project team needs to pay special attention to its operating efficiencies. The initial cost made for an efficient HVAC system will have a short payback period and will result in energy savings through the entire life cycle of the equipment. In the United States, HVAC systems account for 30% of the energy used in commercial buildings and nearly 50% of the energy used in residential buildings.[2]

Increasing the **thermal mass** of a building is another strategy for downsizing the HVAC equipment. Thermal mass is the ability of a material to absorb and store energy, and in most buildings, a lot of heat is required to change the temperature of high-density materials such as concrete and brick. Using thicker exterior brick or similar exterior building layers will result in less electricity usage for the HVAC, as these materials slowly absorb and store heat during the day while keeping the inside temperatures the same.

In appropriate climates, using **natural ventilation** can be another great strategy to reduce energy usage and provide fresh air to the building occupants. By just providing an adequate number of windows and openings, natural ventilation can be achieved.

For mechanically ventilated buildings, the air filters need to be checked regularly, and the dust needs to be cleaned. Otherwise, HVAC equipment will need to use more energy to move the air through the ducts.

Radiant heat flooring and underfloor air distribution can be the other strategies used to address energy efficiency.

Projects can also capture **efficiencies of scale**, and, when possible, multiple buildings can share one HVAC system. By employing district heating and cooling systems, all the sharing buildings can take advantage of lower operating costs.

ENERGY EFFICIENCY FOR LIGHTING

For some buildings, lighting can be the biggest contributor to a building's energy use. Energy is both used for powering the lights and to offset the increased cooling loads resulting from the heat of the lighting. Daylighting is surely the best strategy, as it saves energy and increases the well-being of building occupants.

For artificial lighting, selecting appropriate light bulbs is one of the factors that will affect energy efficiency. **Incandescent lights** will consume more energy and release more heat than other lights. Compact fluorescent lights, high-intensity discharge lamps, and light-emitting diodes (LEDs) can produce more light with less electricity.

Using old fluorescent lights is not a good option. It would be better to replace the existing ones with the new technology fluorescent lights, which will return the outlay costs in a very short period of time.

By installing an adequate number of **lighting controls** for individual users—made up of **photosensors, timers, occupancy sensors**, and **advanced lighting controls**—projects can cut down their lighting costs since these devices will shut off lights when lighting is not needed.

ENERGY EFFICIENCY FOR APPLIANCES

When choosing appliances for building use, project teams need to consider the energy efficiencies of different alternatives. Appliances with ENERGY STAR labels can be a smart choice since their energy-efficiency criteria have been established by the US Department of Energy and US Environmental Protection Agency.

MONITOR AND VERIFY PERFORMANCE

Monitoring and verifying building efficiency performance is essential to ensuring that the building systems are functioning as designed. This can be established through control systems, a building automation system, and commissioning and retrocommissioning. (Retrocommissioning is a systematic process for analyzing and optimizing building system performance.)

A building automation system (BAS), which is a computer-based monitoring system that can monitor, coordinate, and control every individual building system, helps reduce energy usage by identifying faulty building systems or equipment or can track the energy use of all individual items. A building automation system would enable the facility manager to find innovative solutions to address the items with excessive energy usage.

RENEWABLE ENERGY

As the name implies, renewable energy is a type of energy that derives from renewable sources. Renewable energy includes solar, wind, wave, biomass, and geothermal power, plus certain forms of hydropower. The use of renewable energy sources avoids the environmental impacts associated with the production and consumption of nonrenewable fuels, such as coal, nuclear power, oil, and natural gas.

Renewable energy sources can be either on-site or off-site. **On-site renewable energy** production involves a system that generates renewable energy, such as a solar photovoltaic (PV) panel that converts the sun's energy into electricity. **Off-site renewable energy**, which is also called green power, is purchased at a premium price per kilowatt-hour from a utility or a provider of **renewable energy certificates (RECs)**. A key thing to remember is the difference between the on-site renewable energy production and the purchase of green power, which refers to the off-site renewable energy in LEED.

If the local utility provider sells green power, the project can directly purchase and use green power. However, if the local utility company does not sell green power, then the project team can pay an extra fee (often called "**green pricing**") to the local utility company to buy a set quantity of green power instead of buying electricity produced by nonrenewable energy sources. Even though the green energy bought will not be physically used by the project, the utility provider will need to increase its green energy on the electricity grid.

Or instead, the project can buy RECs, which represent a tradable, nontangible commodity associated with the qualities of renewable-energy generation. An REC is a proof that when purchased, an amount of energy was created using renewable-energy sources. If the local utility company in a project team's location does not sell green power, then the project team can offset the building's energy use by purchasing green power from renewable energy projects around the country.

Green-e is the leading certification program for green power generation in the United States. As will be mentioned under the "Green Power and Carbon Offsets" credit, LEED requires projects to use **Green-e Energy certified** green power for earning the credit.

It is also important to mention **carbon offsets,** which allow projects to fund companies or organizations that reduce or remove carbon emissions. An example organization or company may work on reforestation with those funds, or any other activity that would support both the environment and the atmosphere.

A carbon offset is a reduction of carbon dioxide made in order to compensate for, or offset, an equivalent carbon dioxide emission made elsewhere. Since energy use of the green building will result in carbon emissions, green buildings can calculate their carbon emissions from their energy use and purchase the same amount of carbon offsets to compensate for their emissions. The main goal is to establish **carbon neutrality**, which is to emit no more carbon emissions than can realistically be offset. For a carbon offset to qualify in LEED, it needs to be **Green-e Climate certified**.

Carbon footprint is another term that we hear a lot in our everyday lives, which refers to the measure of greenhouse gas emissions associated with an activity, such as construction, operation, transportation, or construction materials.

TYPES OF ON-SITE RENEWABLE ENERGY

1. **Solar power:** Solar power can be categorized under active solar and passive solar.
   a. **Active solar:** This type of solar power converts sunlight into light, heat, or electricity. **PV panels** can convert solar energy to electricity. **Solar thermal collectors** use the solar energy for heating air or water that can then be used in the underfloor heating or air conditioning for buildings—or even for heating swimming pools.

   b. **Passive solar:** This type of solar power deals with optimizing the project design to use sunlight more effectively. As it is a passive strategy, its function is not about generating energy from solar energy via equipment. Orienting the building to maximize solar gains—using shades that do not allow summer sun but allow winter sun into the building—or creating thermal masses to store solar heat are examples of passive solar.

2. **Geothermal heat pumps:** Also known as "geoexchange," or "ground source heat pumps," geothermal heat pumps are central heating and/or cooling systems that transfer heat to or from the ground. In winter, this system uses the earth as a heat source while in summer the earth is used as a heat sink. Geothermal heat pumps should not be confused

with geothermal power, which uses a high-temperature heat source for electricity generation and is only available in the locations with volcanic activity closer to the earth's surface. Geothermal heat pumps can be installed at any location by the installment of pipes that typically go 20 feet (6 meters) underground. The pipes are only responsible for transferring the earth's heat to the building in winter, and they transfer the heat of the building to earth in summer. No cooling towers, chillers, or boilers are needed to use this system, and maintenance costs are low. It is a closed-loop system and uses the same medium for heat transfers.

TYPES OF OFF-SITE RENEWABLE ENERGY

1. **Wind energy:** This type of green power comes from **wind turbines**, which directly convert the energy of the wind to electricity.
2. **Hydro energy:** This type of energy uses the downward running water from lakes or streams to convert water-flow energy into electricity. It requires building a hydroelectric dam.
3. **Biofuel:** Biofuel-based electrical systems can create electricity from biofuels. Typical biofuels include <u>untreated wood waste</u>, <u>landfill gas</u>, <u>agricultural crops or waste</u>, <u>animal waste,</u> and <u>other types of organic waste</u>.
4. **Wave power: Wave energy converters (WEC)** can convert the energy of waves into electricity.
5. **Tidal power:** This is a form of hydropower that converts the energy of tides into electricity.

Figure 11. Off-shore wind turbines (courtesy of Andy Dingley)

ONGOING PERFORMANCE

A green building is not completed at the end of the construction phase. During the building operations phase, it is critical to ensure that a project functions as designed, and it should additionally sustain this performance over time. Performance goals that were set during planning and design may be undermined by construction defects or equipment malfunctions. The entire building should be monitored and verified with the aim of identifying and resolving any problems as they arise.

The actual performance of the building should be compared with building performance measurements from an energy simulation or an industry benchmarking tool. EPA's ENERGY STAR Portfolio Manager comes in very handy, from which users enter data for energy consumption, along with other supporting information, into a free online tool. Portfolio Manager then evaluates the actual performance of the building against that of others with similar characteristics.

LEED also requires projects to implement building commissioning, which will be discussed in depth under the "Fundamental Commissioning and Verification" prerequisite. To summarize, commissioning is a systematic investigation by skilled personnel that compares building performance with the project goals, design specifications, and, most importantly, the owner's project requirements (OPR).

The process begins early in the design, by first specifying the OPRs. These requirements will then be considered throughout the building design and implemented during the construction process; the outcome will eventually form the baseline for evaluation in the building operations phase.

Ongoing commissioning for building operations ensures that the building continues to operate according to its fundamental operational requirements. Even though the commissioning process results in extra costs to the owner, commissioning is one of the most cost-effective solutions for improving building performance and in cutting down operating costs.

Retrocommissioning is basically the same process of commissioning applied to existing buildings. The aim of retrocommissioning is to keep a building on track for meeting or exceeding the original operational goals.

During the ongoing performance implementation, projects need to do the following:

- Adhere to the owner's project requirements (OPR)
- Provide staff training
- Develop a **preventive maintenance program** to keep the building in optimal condition
- Create incentives for occupants and tenants in order to involve them in energy-efficiency strategies such as promoting the use of energy-efficient computers, turning out lights before leaving, and giving them feedback on energy performance

STRATEGIES TO ADDRESS ENERGY AND ATMOSPHERE

- Establish energy-design goals
- Size the building appropriately
- Use free energy as much as possible
- Orient the building in order to minimize energy usage
- Insulate the building
- Address the building envelope
- Implement passive strategies to lower energy usage
- Use natural ventilation where appropriate
- Use high-performance mechanical systems and appliances
- Use high-performance lighting
- Install lighting controls, photosensors, timers, occupancy sensors, and advanced lighting controls
- Use high-efficiency infrastructure
- Conduct energy audits
- Use refrigerants with low ODP and GWP values
- Capture efficiencies of scale
- Develop an energy simulation and compare building performance
- Generate on-site renewable energy
- Purchase off-site renewable energy
- Purchase carbon offsets
- Implement commissioning and retrocommissioning
- Monitor and verify building performance
- Adhere to the owner's project requirements (OPR)
- Provide staff training
- Develop a preventive maintenance program
- Create incentives for occupants and tenants

ENERGY AND ATMOSPHERE PREREQUISITES AND CREDITS

FUNDAMENTAL COMMISSIONING AND VERIFICATION—PREREQUISITE

PREREQUISITE SUMMARY

As a major part of the integrated process, building commissioning ensures that the projects are designed and built as really intended. A well-oriented commissioning process will always lead to fewer change orders, avoidance of project delays and cost overruns, and increased durability of the whole project.

And this prerequisite forces projects to implement a fundamental commissioning and verification process to ensure that the project design and construction meet the owner's project requirements (OPR) and basis of design (BOD). Project teams will additionally create an **operations and maintenance (O&M) plan** that will contain all the necessary information to operate the building efficiently.

By the end of the design development phase, a qualified commissioning authority (CxA) must first be assigned as a third party who should directly report to the owner. The CxA will then review the design and verify that the design meets the OPR and BOD, develop and implement a **commissioning (Cx) plan**, confirm incorporation of Cx requirements into the construction documents, develop construction checklists and test procedures, verify system tests, and prepare a **final Cx report** while documenting all the findings directly to the owner throughout the whole process.

The Cx plan will contain the following:

- Goals and objectives
- Systems to be commissioned
- Team member roles/responsibilities
- OPR reviews
- BOD reviews
- Development of functional tests
- Verification of system performance
- Reporting deficiencies and accepting building systems

The Cx plan will be a living document that will be updated throughout the project, and it will also form the basis of the final Cx report. To ensure designers and engineers are meeting the OPR and BOD, the CxA will periodically conduct Cx meetings.

During construction, the CxA will verify that the contractor is working according to the design. The CxA, as well as the design team or the contractor, will develop construction checklists to be used during the construction phase. Finally, the CxA will execute functional testing among the building elements and systems to make sure everything is installed according to the specifications and the design.

All the data used during the design and construction phase will be compiled by the CxA into a final Cx report, which will contain a Cx process overview, BOD, submittals, design review log, Cx specifications, installation verifications, functional performance tests, and an issues log.

To assist the building operations phase, the CxA will prepare a **current facility requirements (CFR)** and operations and maintenance (O&M) plan that will contain all the information to operate the building efficiently (equipment run-time schedules, building-occupancy schedules, lighting levels of the building, minimum outside air requirements, sequences of operations for the building, and other information.)

Systems that will be a part of the fundamental commissioning process are:

- HVAC and plumbing, including domestic hot water systems, pumps, and controls
- Electrical, including service, distribution, lighting, and controls, including daylighting controls
- Renewable energy systems

Systems that are not required to be commissioned under this prerequisite but may be added to the Cx scope with the request of the owner include the following:

- Building envelope
- Life safety systems
- Communications and data systems
- Fire protection and fire alarm systems
- Process equipment

The OPR and BOD should cover the building envelope, which means that the design of the building envelope should be reviewed even if the project teams choose not to perform an envelope commissioning during the construction phase. Project teams may also choose to pursue the "Enhanced Commissioning" credit, which awards points for building envelope commissioning during the construction phase.

PREREQUISITE INTENT

Supporting the design, construction, and operations of the building, which meet the owner's project requirements for energy, water, indoor environmental quality, and durability.

PREREQUISITE REQUIREMENTS

Commission mechanical, electrical, plumbing, and renewable energy systems and assemblies according to **ASHRAE Guideline 0-2005**, and **ASHRAE Guideline 1.1-2007** for the HVAC&R (heating, ventilating, air-conditioning and refrigeration) systems.

For the building envelope, the requirements are limited to review of the OPR, the BOD, and the project design. **NIBS Guideline 3-2012 for Exterior Enclosures** can also provide additional guidance on building envelope commissioning.

Scope of the commissioning process:

The commissioning authority must do the following:

- Review the OPR, the BOD, and the project design
- Develop and implement the commissioning plan
- Ensure that the Cx requirements are integrated into the construction documents
- Prepare construction checklists and system test procedures
- Confirm system test execution
- Prepare the issues and benefits log throughout the Cx process
- Prepare the final Cx report
- Report all the findings directly to the owner

For reviewing the building envelope design, a qualified member of the design or construction team (who is not in the exterior envelope design team) can also be chosen.

Commissioning Authority (CxA):

The qualified CxA should have completed commissioning for at least two similar projects from the early design phase to the minimum ten months of occupancy. The CxA can be an independent consultant, owner's employee, disinterested subcontractor of the design and construction team, or employee of the design or construction team who is not part of the project. The CxA can be a member of the construction or design team as well if the project is smaller than 20,000 square feet.

It is important to note that in all the conditions, the CxA should report directly to the owner.

Current Facilities Requirements (CFR) and Operations and Maintenance (O&M) plan:
The CxA should prepare the CFR and the O&M plan, which should include the following:

- A schedule for building occupancy
- Run-time schedule for equipment
- Sequence of operations for the building
- HVAC equipment setpoints
- Building lighting levels
- Minimum requirements for outside air
- Systems narrative and preventive maintenance plan about mechanical and electrical systems and equipment
- Periodic commissioning requirements

KEY THINGS TO REMEMBER

- ASHRAE Guideline 0-2005 and ASHRAE Guideline 1.1-2007 (for HVAC&R systems) are used for commissioning.
- CxA must always report directly to the owner.
- In the fundamental commissioning, the CxA can be an independent consultant, an owner's employee, a disinterested subcontractor of the design and construction team, or an employee of the design or construction team who is not part of the project.
- The qualified CxA should have completed commissioning for at least two similar projects from the early design phase to the minimum ten months of occupancy.
- The purpose and elements of the Cx plan, the final Cx report, and the CFR and O&M plan.

MINIMUM ENERGY PERFORMANCE—PREREQUISITE

PREREQUISITE SUMMARY

Just as the "Water Use Reduction" prerequisite aims to decrease potable water usage of a building, this prerequisite aims to establish a minimum energy performance.

In option 1, the project team can perform a whole-building energy simulation, according to the **ANSI/ASHRAE/IESNA Standard 90.1.-2010, Appendix G with errata.** This allows work to start on the model by applying different strategies to establish a minimum of **5%** reduction in energy costs. (A 5% reduction is required by the prerequisite if the project team chooses to perform a whole-building energy simulation.)

Instead of performing a whole-building energy simulation and establishing a 5% reduction in the energy costs, the project team can choose to achieve prescriptive compliance to the **ASHRAE 50% Advanced Energy Design Guide** in option 2, or to the **Advanced Buildings**™ **Core Performance Guide**™ in option 3 by additionally complying with the **ANSI/ASHRAE/IESNA Standard 90.1.-2010, with errata** for both options 2 and 3.

When doing a whole-building energy simulation in option 1, the projects must establish reduced energy costs without including renewable energy sources in their calculations. And the energy calculations should take into account both the **process energy** (**unregulated energy**) and the **nonprocess energy** (**regulated energy**).

Process energy, or unregulated energy, includes:

- Computers
- Office equipment
- Kitchen stoves
- Kitchen refrigerators
- Cooking and food preparation equipment
- Washers and dryers
- Elevators and escalators

Please note that most of the items above work by being connected to a plug, with the exception of elevators and escalators.

The term "process load" is synonymously used with **plug loads** (receptacle loads), which represent the electrical use by all the equipment that is connected to the electrical system via electrical receptacle. Therefore, the energy consumed while charging the battery of a cell phone would be considered as a plug load as well as a process load.

Nonprocess, or regulated, energy includes items that are used to condition spaces and maintain comfort and amenities for building occupants:

- Interior and exterior lighting (parking garage, security, landscape, architectural lighting)
- HVAC (heating, cooling, fans, pumps)
- Hot water heating
- Toilet exhaust
- Parking garage ventilation

With the consumption of process energy in the building, **building process loads** occur; with the consumption of nonprocess energy, **building nonprocess loads** occur.

PREREQUISITE INTENT

Reducing the economic and environmental harms resulting from excessive energy use by implementing a minimum level of energy efficiency for the building and its systems.

PREREQUISITE REQUIREMENTS

Option 1: Whole-building energy simulation
Create the building model and simulate whole-building energy use. Calculate the baseline building performance according to **ANSI/ASHRAE/IESNA Standard 90.1.-2010, Appendix G with errata**. Demonstrate a **5%** improvement in the baseline building performance by implementing a new design, which should also comply with the mentioned standard.

The simulation should include all the energy consumption and costs associated with the project as well as the unregulated loads. COMNET Modeling Guidelines and Procedures can be used to implement measures for reducing the unregulated loads.

Option 2: Prescriptive compliance: the ASHRAE 50% Advanced Energy Design Guide
Comply with the mandatory and prescriptive provisions of **ANSI/ASHRAE/IESNA Standard 90.1.-2010, with errata**. In addition, the project should comply with the HVAC and service water heating requirements of the **ASHRAE 50% Advanced Energy Design Guide**.

Option 3: Prescriptive compliance: Advanced Buildings™ Core Performance™ Guide
(To be able to pursue this option, the project should be less than 100,000 square feet.)

The project should comply with the mandatory and prescriptive provisions of **ANSI/ASHRAE/IESNA Standard 90.1.-2010, with errata**. In addition, the project should comply with the Advanced Buildings™ Core Performance™ Guide (CPG).

In this option, the energy performance target should be established using ENERGY STAR's Target Finder, and a minimum score of 90 should be achieved.

This prerequisite also has a credit—"Optimize Energy Performance"—that will be discussed in the following pages. The credit awards points for making further reductions in the energy costs according to the percentage of reductions.

The credit has two options: the first option is exactly the same as this prerequisite, which entails whole-building energy simulation, and the second option is prescriptive compliance with the ASHRAE Advanced Energy Design Guide. Projects that wish to pursue option 1 of the credit should choose option 1 of this prerequisite.

To pursue the maximum number of points in the "Optimize Energy Performance" credit, the project will need to choose option 1 since it contains the most points (18).

KEY THINGS TO REMEMBER

- The ANSI/ASHRAE/IESNA Standard 90.1.-2010.
- The ASHRAE 50% Advanced Energy Design Guide.
- The Advanced Buildings™ Core Performance™ Guide.
- The COMNET Modeling Guidelines and Procedures.
- The definitions and examples of process energy (unregulated energy), nonprocess energy (regulated energy), process loads, nonprocess loads, and plug loads.

BUILDING-LEVEL ENERGY METERING—PREREQUISITE

PREREQUISITE SUMMARY

Similar to the "Building-Level Water Metering" prerequisite, this prerequisite requires the tracking of total building energy consumption by installing energy meters or submeters for all the energy sources that serve the building.

All projects should commit to sharing their energy consumption and electrical demand data for five years, starting from the LEED certification date or date of occupancy, whichever comes first. USGBC will then collect and analyze data in order to identify common traits among high and low performers, and it will share its findings with the project teams so that they can improve their performance.

PREREQUISITE INTENT

Tracking building-level energy use to discover opportunities for energy savings and to support energy management.

PREREQUISITE REQUIREMENTS

Install new or use existing building-level energy meters/submeters that can provide data on total building energy consumption from various sources, including <u>electricity</u>, <u>natural gas</u>, <u>chilled water, steam</u>, <u>fuel oil</u>, <u>propane,</u> and <u>biomass</u>. Utility-owned meters capable of tracking total building energy consumption will be also acceptable.

The total building energy consumption and electrical demand data (if metered) should be shared with USGBC at a minimum of **one month intervals for a five-year period or until the building changes ownership or lessee.** Data sharing should start on the date the project accepts LEED certification.

KEY THINGS TO REMEMBER

- There are two reasons why USGBC collects water usage data: USGBC will collect and analyze data in order to identify common traits among high and low performers, and it will also share its findings with the project teams so that they can improve their performance.
- In LEED, all projects should share their total energy usage for a five-year period, at a minimum of one month intervals, starting from the LEED certification date.
- Electricity, natural gas, chilled water, steam, fuel oil, propane, and biomass energy sources all need to be included in the energy metering.

FUNDEMENTAL REFRIGERANT MANAGEMENT—PREREQUISITE

PREREQUISITE SUMMARY

Chlorofluorocarbons (CFCs) are one of the primary causes of ozone depletion, and ozone depletion is primarily addressed by a building's energy use and the types of refrigerants used.

This prerequisite aims to reduce ozone depletion by prohibiting the use of chlorofluorocarbon (CFC)-based refrigerants in the HVAC&R systems. If the project is reusing existing HVAC&R systems, the project team should complete a **CFC phase-out conversion before project completion**. (Equipment that contains less than 0.5 pound [225 grams] of refrigerant will be exempt.)

In 1987, the Montreal Protocol was established in order to phase out the use of the most harmful ozone-depleting substances, including CFCs. Through the Montreal Protocol, CFC production was phased out before 1995 in the countries that signed the protocol. Before 2010, CFC production was phased out in most of the other countries. Even so, many CFCs still remain in a large number of existing products. With the CFC phase-out requirement, this prerequisite aims to support the Montreal Protocol.

Even though the **CFCs**, **HCFCs** (hydrochlorofluorocarbons), and **halons** (chemicals used in fire suppression systems) all contribute to ozone depletion, this prerequisite only addresses CFCs.

PREREQUISITE INTENT

Reducing stratospheric ozone depletion.

PREREQUISITE REQUIREMENTS

Do not use chlorofluorocarbon (CFC)-based refrigerants in HVAC&R systems. When reusing existing HVAC&R equipment, complete a **comprehensive CFC phase-out conversion** before project completion. Phase-out plans extending beyond the project completion date will be considered on their merits.

Existing small HVAC&R or other equipment—such as standard refrigerators or small water cooler units containing less than **0.5 pound** (225 grams) of refrigerant—are exempt.

KEY THINGS TO REMEMBER

- Expect to see several questions relating to refrigerants. In the exam, refrigerant questions are the most favored.

- When using existing HVAC&R units, comprehensive CFC phase-out conversion should be completed before the project's completion.

- Existing small HVAC&R or other equipment—such as standard refrigerators and small water cooler units containing less than **0.5 pound** (225 grams) of refrigerant—are exempt from LEED requirements.

- The Montreal Protocol is an international agreement signed in 1987 to phase out the use of most harmful ozone-depleting substances, including CFCs. Through the Montreal Protocol, CFC production was phased out before **1995** in the countries that signed the protocol. Before **2010**, CFC production was phased out in most of the other countries.

- Even though halons are not addressed by this prerequisite, it's good to know that they're another type of chemical, used mainly in fire suppression systems, that also causes ozone depletion.

ENHANCED COMMISSIONING—CREDIT

- 2–6 Points

CREDIT SUMMARY

This is the credit of the "Fundamental Commissioning and Verification" prerequisite, which requires additional obligations.

In this credit's option 1, project teams can choose to implement enhanced systems commissioning. In this instance, the CxA will additionally review the contractor submittals, verify operator and occupant training requirements, review the building operations ten months after substantial completion, and provide an ongoing commissioning plan, among other tasks.

In addition to implementing enhanced systems commissioning, project teams can also choose to implement **monitor-based commissioning (MBCx)** to gain additional points in option 1. MBCx is the process of utilizing a software that will monitor real-time data from the building automation system and building meters. The automated system should be able to detect faulty equipment and discover unusual energy usages as they occur.

In this credit's option 2, the project teams will need to perform **building envelope commissioning (BECx)**. BECx will ensure that the building envelope is tested and verified to achieve the target building performance with respect to energy, water, indoor environmental quality, and durability. BECx increases the occupants' comfort levels through infiltration testing, reduced solar heat gain, and glare control. The envelope commissioning process should start in the design phase.

Project teams may choose to pursue both options 1 and 2 to earn full points from this credit.

CREDIT INTENT

The intent of this credit is to implement enhanced commissioning measures that will further support the design, construction, and operation of a project that meets the target requirements for energy, water, indoor environmental quality, and durability defined in the OPR.

CREDIT REQUIREMENTS

Commissioning Authority:

As with the "Fundamental Commissioning and Verification" prerequisite, the qualified CxA should have completed commissioning for at least two similar projects from the early design phase to the minimum ten months of occupancy. In enhanced commissionining, the CxA can only be an <u>independent consultant</u>, <u>owner's employee</u>, or <u>a disinterested subcontractor of the design team</u>.

Option 1: Enhanced systems commissioning—3–4 Points

Path 1: Enhanced commissioning—3 points

As with the "Fundamental Commissioning and Verification" prerequisite, complete the commissioning process according to **ASHRAE Guideline 0-2005** and **ASHRAE Guideline 1.1-2007 for HVAC&R systems**. This is for electrical, mechanical, plumbing, and renewable energy systems as they relate to energy, water, indoor environmental quality, and durability.

The CxA should **review the contractor submittals,** and;

- Verify inclusion of systems manual requirements in construction documents
- Verify inclusion of operator and training requirements in construction documents
- Verify systems manual updates
- Verify **operator and occupant training delivery and effectiveness**
- Verify seasonal testing
- Review the building operations **10 months after project completion** (called **postconstruction verification**)
- Develop an **ongoing commissioning plan**

All the tasks of the enhanced commissioning process must be included in the OPR and BOD.

OR

Path 2: Enhanced and monitoring-based commissioning—4 points

In addition to all the requirements in "Path 1: Enhanced commissioning," monitoring-based commissioning should be implemented. Monitoring-based procedures must be developed, and measurement points need to be determined to assess the performance of the energy- and water-consuming systems. Additionally, measurement requirements, limits of acceptable values, training, repair plans, and roles and responsibilities should be addressed. These procedures, as well as the measurement points, should be included in the commissioning plan.

AND/OR

Option 2: Envelope Commissioning—2 Points

In the "Fundamental Commissioning and Verification" prerequisite, the building envelope design needs to be reviewed, as there will be sections about the building envelope in the OPR and BOD. In this option, the commissioning process (CxP) for the building envelope will be conducted according to **ASHRAE Guideline 0-2005** and the **National Institute of Building Sciences (NIBS) Guideline 3-2012, Exterior Enclosure Technical Requirements for the Cx Process**. And in this instance the CxA will review the contractor submittals for the building envelope as well as the envelope testing. Additionally, operator training and review of the envelope operations will be completed.

KEY THINGS TO REMEMBER

- In enhanced commissioning, the CxA can be an independent consultant, an owner's employee, or a disinterested subcontractor of the design team.
- For the enhanced commissioning, the CxA will review the contractor submittals, verify the operator and occupant trainings' delivery and effectiveness, conduct a postconstruction verification ten months after project completion, and develop an ongoing commissioning plan.
- ASHRAE Guideline 0-2005.
- ASHRAE Guideline 1.1-2007 (for HVAC&R Systems).
- National Institute of Building Sciences (NIBS) Guideline 3-2012.

OPTIMIZE ENERGY PERFORMANCE—CREDIT

- **1–18 Points** (the credit that contains the most points)

CREDIT SUMMARY

This is the credit of the "Minimum Energy Performance" prerequisite, which aims for further energy reductions.

In credit's option 1, projects can use their whole-building energy simulation (if they choose to create it by pursuing option 1 in the prerequisite), and make further reductions from their baseline energy use of 6% to 50%. However, projects cannot include renewable energy sources to reduce the energy costs for this credit.

In credit's option 2, projects need to achieve compliance to the **ASHRAE Advanced Energy Design Guide.**

To pursue option 1 of this credit, projects need to pursue option 1 of the "Minimum Energy Performance" prerequisite. To pursue option 2 of this credit, the prerequisite's option 2 should be pursued.

CREDIT INTENT

This credit intends to achieve further levels of energy-efficient performance beyond its prerequisite standards for reducing economic and environmental harms that arise from excessive energy use.

CREDIT REQUIREMENTS

Identify the project's climate zone according to **ASHRAE 90.1-2010**, Appendix B, set energy performance targets no later than the schematic design phase, and choose one of the two options:

Option 1: Whole-building energy simulation—1–18 Points
Follow the criteria in option 1 of the "Minimum Energy Performance" prerequisite and improve the building's energy performance. Projects will be awarded points according to their percentage of annual energy cost savings. Projects that make a reduction of 6% will get 1 point, and projects that make a reduction of 50% will get the full 18 points.

Project teams that pursue the "Integrative Process" credit should complete the simple box energy modeling for that credit and then complete the whole-building energy simulation for this credit. Simple box energy modeling is a preliminary energy simulation; however, the whole-building energy simulation is much more detailed.

OR

Option 2: Prescriptive compliance: ASHRAE Advanced Energy Design Guide—1–6 Points
Implement and document compliance with the ASHRAE 50% Advanced Energy Design Guide and climate zone.

KEY THINGS TO REMEMBER

- ASHRAE 50% Advanced Energy Design Guide,
- In LEED, the project teams should identify their project's climate zone according to ASHRAE 90.1-2010.
- The percentage improvement in energy performance is calculated by using the energy cost savings, not energy use.

ADVANCED ENERGY METERING—CREDIT

- ▪ 1 Point

CREDIT SUMMARY

This is the credit of the "Building-Level Energy Metering" prerequisite, which requires projects to provide energy metering to whole-building energy sources and also to any individual energy end use that consumes more than 10% of the total annual energy consumed by the building.

CREDIT INTENT

To further support energy management and encourage discovery of opportunities for extra energy savings by tracking building-level and system-level energy use.

CREDIT REQUIREMENTS

Install advanced energy metering for the following:
- ➤ All whole-building energy sources used by the building
- ➤ Any individual energy end uses that consume **10%** or more of the total annual consumption of the building

The advanced energy metering should meet the following characteristics:
- ➤ Meters should be permanently installed, be able to record at intervals of one hour or less, and transmit data to a remote location. Additionally, meters should be capable of reporting hourly, daily, monthly, and annual energy use.
- ➤ Electricity meters should record both the energy consumption and the energy demand. If appropriate, the whole-building electricity meters should record the power factor.
- ➤ The data collection system should be connected to a local area network, building automation system, wireless network, or comparable communication infrastructure.
- ➤ The system must be able to store all meter data for at least 36 months.

KEY THINGS TO REMEMBER

- ■ In LEED, any individual energy end uses that consume **10%** or more of the total annual consumption of the building should be tracked <u>separately</u> for advanced energy metering.

DEMAND RESPONSE—CREDIT

- 1–2 Points

CREDIT SUMMARY

Think about a power plant that serves the whole city and imagine that the weather gets extremely hot beyond the normal average temperature. As a consequence, everyone simultaneously turns on his or her air conditioner, creating a sudden increase in electricity demand.

If the power plant's energy is not enough to handle that peak demand, then the utility company would think about constructing an additional plant, or it would need to find additional generation sources, including nonrenewable energy sources.

Demand response is a technology that aims to overcome these types of conflicts by reducing energy demand, especially during peak times. The utility company sends an alert, which is called a **DR event** or a **curtailment event**, to commercial customers who agree to change their usage patterns at peak demands. In turn, the commercial consumers reduce their demand with the alert. Consumers are rewarded for their participation in the demand response programs, and the construction of additional power plants is avoided. In some cities, utility companies may charge extra during peak times in order to reduce energy demand.

On top of this, demand response programs are helpful in balancing the supply of renewable energy sources. For example, a solar energy source will not be able generate power at nights, which will therefore lower the power availability; a demand response program can offset this effect.

Projects that participate in demand response programs will earn this credit. However, if there isn't any available demand response program in the project's location, the credit can still be earned by providing infrastructure for future demand response programs.

CREDIT INTENT

To promote participation in demand response technologies and programs that enable more efficient energy generation and distribution systems, increase grid reliability, and reduce greenhouse gases.

CREDIT REQUIREMENTS

Design the building and equipment to allow participation in demand response programs through **load shedding** or **load shifting**. On-site electricity generation does not meet the intent of this credit.

Load shedding is the intentional action by the power utility to reduce the load in the power system in order to prevent a total failure of the system. Load shifting is storing the energy generated during off-peak hours to use it during peak-demand hours. Usually, battery systems are used to store the energy during load shifting.

Case 1: Demand response program available—2 points

Participate in a demand response (DR) program and complete the following activities:

➤ Design a fully automated DR system based on external initiation by a DR Program Provider. A semiautomated DR may also be utilized in practice.

➤ Enroll in a minimum one year DR program, for at least 10% of the estimated peak electricity demand. Peak demand is determined under the "Minimum Energy Performance" prerequisite.

➤ Develop a plan for meeting the DR commitment during the DR event.

➤ Include the DR processes in the CxA's scope of work, including participation in at least one full test of the DR plan.

Case 2: Demand response program not available - 1 point

Provide infrastructure for future demand response programs and complete the following activities:

➤ Install interval recording meters with communications and ability for the building automation system to accept an external price or control signal.

➤ Develop a comprehensive plan for shedding at least 10% of building estimated peak electricity demand. Peak demand should be determined under the "Minimum Energy Performance" prerequisite.

➤ Include the CxA in the DR processes, including one full DR testing.

➤ Contact the local utility to discuss participation in future DR programs.

KEY THINGS TO REMEMBER

- Project teams need to design the building and equipment to allow participation in demand response programs through **load shedding** or **shifting**.
- The definitions of load shedding and load shifting.
- If a demand response program is not available in a project's location, projects can still provide infrastructure for future demand response programs and earn the credit.

RENEWABLE ENERGY PRODUCTION—CREDIT

- 1–3 Points

CREDIT SUMMARY

Using energy from renewable energy sources saves both the environment and human health by reducing carbon emissions as well as air pollution. This credit aims to award the projects that produce renewable energy on-site or the projects that sign an energy use agreement with a renewable energy provider in the same utility service area. Producing renewable energy on-site will also aid in eliminating the waste that occurs during electricity transmission.

Green power will be discussed later in this chapter under the "Green Power and Carbon Offsets" credit, which will address the renewable energy produced off-site. One aspect of this credit is that projects can still earn the credit as long as the renewable energy provider that sells green power is in the same utility service area.

CREDIT INTENT

Reducing both the environmental and economic harms related to fossil fuel energy by increasing the use of self-supply of renewable energy.

CREDIT REQUIREMENTS

Use on-site renewable energy systems to offset building energy costs. The percentage of renewable energy will be calculated with the following equation:

$$\text{\% renewable energy} = \frac{\text{Equivalent cost of usable energy produced by the renewable energy system}}{\text{Total building energy cost}}$$

If there was pursuit of option 1 of the "Minimum Energy Performance" prerequisite—which calculates total building energy cost with a simulation—projects could use that cost as the total building energy cost in the formula above. Otherwise, projects can use the US Department of Energy's Commercial Buildings Energy Consumption Survey (CBECS) database to estimate the total building energy cost.

The use of <u>solar gardens</u> or <u>community renewable energy systems</u> is also allowed if both of the requirements below are met:

➤ The project owns the system or leased the system for a period of at least **10 years.**

➤ The system is located within the **same utility** service area.

Points will be awarded according to the project's percentage of renewable energy use shown in the table below:

Percentage of renewable energy	Points
1%	1
5%	2
10%	3

Table 17

Eligible renewable energy sources include <u>photovoltaic</u>, <u>solar thermal</u>, <u>wind</u>, <u>biofuel</u>, <u>low-impact hydroelectricity</u>, <u>wave</u> and <u>tidal,</u> and <u>geothermal energy</u>.

KEY THINGS TO REMEMBER

■ In LEED, renewable energy calculations are based on energy costs, not energy usage.

■ The use of the US Department of Energy's Commercial Buildings Energy Consumption Survey (CBECS).

ENHANCED REFRIGERANT MANAGEMENT—CREDIT

- 1 Point

CREDIT SUMMARY

This is the credit of the "Fundamental Refrigerant Management" prerequisite. Remember that the prerequisite only addressees CFCs; however, there are more refrigerants that harm the environment, such as HCFCs.

Ozone depletion and global warming are heavily linked with a building's energy use and choice of refrigerants. This credit evaluates the refrigerants used in the project according to their ozone depletion potentials (ODP) and the global warming potentials (GWP) (prerequisite only addresses ODP and not the GWP). Refrigerants like CFCs and HCFCs deplete the ozone layer, as well as increase the global warming rates.

To earn the credit, the projects should either use no refrigerants or only use refrigerants which have a "zero" ozone depletion potential (ODP) and a global warming potential (GWP) of less than 50. If some of the refrigerants exceed those limits, then in credit's option 2, the project can perform a weighted calculation of all the refrigerants used.

CREDIT INTENT

Reducing ozone depletion promoting early compliance with the Montreal Protocol, and reducing contribution to climate change.

CREDIT REQUIREMENTS

Option 1: No refrigerants or low-impact refrigerants—1 point
Do not use any refrigerants or only use naturally occurring or synthetic refrigerants that have an ozone depletion potential (ODP) of zero and a global warming potential (GWP) of less than 50.

OR

Option 2: Calculation of refrigerant impact—1 point
Select refrigerants to be used in HVAC&R equipment to minimize or eliminate the emission of compounds that contribute to ozone depletion and climate change, by performing weighted average calculations for all the refrigerants used.

Ozone Depletion and Global Warming Potentials of Common Refrigerants			
Refrigerant	ODPr	GWPr	Common building application
Chlorofluorocarbons			
CFC-11	1.0	4,68	Centrifugal chiller
CFC-12	1.0	10,72	Refrigerators, chiller
CFC-114	0.94	9,8	Centrifugal chiller
CFC-500	0.605	7,9	Centrifugal chiller, humidifier
CFC-502	0.221	4,6	Low-temp refrigeration
Hydrochlorofluorocarbons			
HCFC-22	0.04	1,78	Air conditioning, chiller
HCFC-123	0.02	76	CFC-11 replacement
Hydrofluorocarbons			
HFC-23	~0	12,24	Ultra-low-temperature refrigeration
HFC-134a	~0	1,32	CFC-12 or HCFC-22 replacement
HFC-245fa	~0	1,02	Insulation agent, centrifugal chiller
HFC-404A	~0	3,9	Low-temperature refrigeration
HFC-407C	~0	1,7	HFC-22 replacement
HFC-410A	~0	1,89	Air-conditioning
HFC-507A	~0	3,9	Low-temperature refrigeration
Natural refrigerants			
Carbon dioxide (CO_2)	0	1	
Ammonia (NH_3)	0	0	
Propane	0	3	

Table 18. Ozone Depletion and Global Warming Potentials of Common Refrigerants

This table is the most important table to know for the exam. Knowing the types, names, and common building applications of these refrigerants is essential. It is even possible to get a question asking for the replacement of HCFC-123. Please note that natural refrigerants do not have any ozone depletion potential and HFCs' ozone depletion potentials are very close to zero.

KEY THINGS TO REMEMBER

■ Table 18
■ In LEED, enhanced refrigerant management addresses both the ODP and the GWP.

GREEN POWER AND CARBON OFFSETS—CREDIT

- 1–2 Points

CREDIT SUMMARY

The credit encourages the projects to buy green power, carbon offsets, and renewable energy certificates (RECs) that correspond to either 50% or 100% of the project's energy use.

CREDIT INTENT

Promoting the use of grid-source, renewable energy technologies, and carbon mitigation projects to encourage the reduction of greenhouse gas emissions.

CREDIT REQUIREMENTS

Engage in a contract for a **minimum of five years** for the qualified resources that have come online since January 1, 2005, to be delivered at least annually. The contract should specify the provision of at least **50%** or **100%** of the project's energy from green power, carbon offsets, or renewable energy certificates (RECs).

Green power and RECs should be **Green-e Energy certified** or the equivalent. RECs can only be used to mitigate the effects of **scope 2**, electricity use.

Carbon offsets may be used to mitigate **scope 1** or **scope 2** emissions on a metric ton of carbon dioxide-equivalent basis, and should be **Green-e Climate certified** or the equivalent.

For projects located in the United States, the carbon offsets must be from greenhouse gas emission reduction projects within the United States.

Determine the percentage of green power or offsets based on the quantity of energy consumed. Points will be awarded according to the following table.

Percentage of building's total energy addressed by green power, RECs and/or offsets	Points
50%	1
100%	2

Table 19

If option 1 of the "Minimum Energy Performance" prerequisite was pursued, the calculated total energy cost for the building could be used to calculate the amount of green power, RECs, and/or carbon offsets required under this credit. Otherwise, projects can use the <u>US Department of Energy's Commercial Buildings Energy Consumption Survey (CBECS)</u> database to estimate the total building energy cost.

KEY THINGS TO REMEMBER

- Definitions of green power, carbon offsets, and RECs
- Green-e Energy certification.
- Green-e Climate certification.
- In LEED, the US Department of Energy's Commercial Buildings Energy Consumption Survey (CBECS) is always used to estimate a building's energy usage/cost, if the project teams did not choose to create a building energy model.
- Sources of scope 1, 2, and 3 emissions (see chapter 1).

CHAPTER 9

MATERIALS AND RESOURCES (MR)

Construction and demolition waste constitutes about 40% of the total solid waste stream in the United States.[1] However, there are much better alternatives than classifying items as waste, and there are many ways to reduce the environmental harm associated with materials. Using fewer materials, choosing environmentally preferable materials, using locally harvested materials, and eliminating waste all provide great benefits.

A systems-based, life-cycle perspective and an integrative process will help projects achieve their goals when addressing the use of materials and resources. Life-cycle assessment, which was discussed in the previous chapters, will also serve as a great tool to evaluate materials and resources according to their environmental performances.

This chapter will discuss both the importance of materials and resources for the environment and their effects on the green building design. After discussing the MR credit category, the book will go over all the MR prerequisites and credits individually to show how these features are used in LEED certification for a LEED BD+C: New Construction and Major Renovation project.

The MR credit category will be discussed under four major sections:
- Conservation of materials
- Environmentally preferable materials
- Waste management and reduction
- Sustainable purchasing

CONSERVATION OF MATERIALS

The conservation of materials starts by eliminating the need for materials during the planning and design phases. Rightsizing the project is the first step toward conservation of materials. An example of rightsizing includes designing buildings that are not larger than really needed and will therefore require fewer materials and resources. The same logic also applies to neighborhoods, as denser and more compact mixed-use neighborhoods will require fewer miles of roads and less infrastructure.

Reusing existing materials, salvaged materials, and especially existing buildings results in tremendous material savings. If the project is a major renovation of an existing building, the project team should look for ways to reuse the following existing materials:
- Framing
- Envelopes
- Walls
- Flooring
- Ceilings
- Roofing

Using salvaged materials will contribute to reduction in the demand for virgin materials. Following are some types of salvaged materials that can be used in new buildings:
- Bricks
- Doors
- Windows
- Flooring
- Cabinets, furniture
- Tiles

Adaptive reuse strategies, which can also be called "designing for flexibility," should be well considered in the buildings that may need frequent changes in layouts or floor plans. For example, a flexible floor plan for a hospital building can allow simple changes to be made regarding the sizes of rooms due to the changes in medical equipment that occur alongside the rapid evolution of the technology.

Through the use of movable wall partitions or the use of modular systems, the layout of the hospital plans can be changed without going into a complete renovation.

Using efficient framing techniques can be another strategy to conserve materials by reducing the amount of materials needed. With advanced framing, if studs can be spaced 24 inches apart instead of 16 inches, fewer materials will be needed without reducing structural performance.

According to the EPA, the best way to eliminate waste is through **source reduction**. Source reduction refers to the exact sizing of the materials to be produced through prefabrication, modular construction, or similar methods, so that no waste is generated on-site. Since it's about decreasing the unnecessary material brought into a building, it also covers the use of products with less packaging.

The conservation of materials does not end with the completion of the construction phase. In a green building, the same principles should be applied throughout the building operations phase to the last phase of the building—a demolition or reuse phase.

ENVIRONMENTALLY PREFERABLE MATERIALS

When selecting materials to be used in the project, the project team should consider a material's entire life cycle or life cycles since the aim of a sustainable material should be to have infinite life cycles. After the useful life of a material ends in one building, the material should be used as another product or a part of another product in order to continue being used. In other words, the first goal here is to implement all the strategies to stop the material from going to landfills as waste.

The second goal should be to evaluate the effects of a particular product on the environment. During their life cycles, all buildings and building materials have different impacts on the environment. The building materials are harvested/extracted, manufactured in the factories, and then installed in the buildings to be used. After that, they either get demolished, disposed, or recycled. Energy is also consumed during each of these stages.

In addition, the way that manufacturers, contractors, or individuals manage each of these steps will vary for each manufacturer, contractor, or consumer. Materials that get extracted or harvested in a sourceful manner, get manufactured in environmentally friendly facilities, and can be recycled to be a part of another product should be less harmful to the environment than regular products. Or, a product that requires lots of energy consumption for extraction and is also not very durable cannot be considered as environmentally friendly.

Using locally produced materials is another plus. An environmentally friendly recyclable material that was extracted in China, manufactured in Germany, and brought to the United States cannot be considered environmentally friendly after all the greenhouse gas emissions that occurred during transportation.

Several credits under this credit category ("Building Product Disclosure and Optimization" credits) provide a location valuation factor, which means that if the purchased products or materials are extracted, manufactured, and purchased within **100 miles (160 kilometers)** of the project, LEED will award the project in the credit calculations by valuing those products at **200%** of their cost.

Below are some features of environmentally preferable materials:

- Locally harvested/extracted and manufactured (which also means less fuel usage during transportation)
- Sustainably grown and harvested
- Made from **rapidly renewable materials** (which can replenish within 10 years)
- Do not contain any toxins
- Manufactured in factories that support human health and workers' rights
- Long-lasting and reusable
- Contain recycled content
- Have intended end-of-life scenarios that avoid a landfill
- Low in embodied energy

To take the discussion to the next level, the following topics will describe the tools and processes that will enable the project teams to make the best decisions on selecting environmentally preferable materials.

LIFE-CYCLE ASSESSMENT

Life-cycle assessment (LCA), which examines all the environmental effects of a product (or even a building) quantitatively during an entire life cycle, can allow project teams to see the background of the building products. A **cradle-to-grave** approach, and, even further, a **cradle-to-cradle** approach, is used in LCA, allowing both the total energy use and other environmental consequences resulting from the creation of that material to be calculated.

The benefits of conducting an LCA can be to see the trade-offs between different materials and to select the materials that would be the best fit for the project and the environment. Instead, the project teams may decide not to use some materials and reduce the total amount of materials in the building, which is also called **dematerialization**.

A cradle-to-cradle approach analyzes a product's life cycle from the first resource extraction/harvesting of the product to its new life as another product or as a part of another product. Thus, cradle-to-cradle products are waste-free products that can be recycled—with their high recyclable content—and reused.

On the other hand, a cradle-to-grave approach analyzes a product's life cycle from the first resource extraction/harvesting of the product to the end of its life, resulting in a form of waste.

Since cradle-to-grave products cannot be recycled, they only have one life cycle, and they all end up in landfills.

For exam purposes, it is also important to be aware of the **cradle-to-gate assessment**, which some manufacturers choose to conduct in order to evaluate a product's partial life cycle—from its resource extraction/harvesting to its becoming a manufactured product ready for sale at the factory gate.

Cradle-to-Cradle Products Innovation Institute developed a **Cradle-to-Cradle certification** that evaluates the environmental aspects of products with five different criteria: material health, material reutilization, renewable energy and carbon management, water stewardship, and social fairness. Cradle-to-Cradle certified products are proven to be environmentally friendly.

PRODUCT TRANSPARENCY

Project teams should be careful about **greenwashing** when selecting products, which refers to the presentation of a product or a material as being more environmentally friendly than it actually is. Environmentally preferable materials should provide accurate and transparent information and declarations to the buyers.

Let's consider the **Environmental Product Declaration (EPD)**, which looks at the entire life cycle of a product and assesses the cost of the product on the environment. Products that contain an EPD will give information about a product's impact on global warming, ozone depletion, water pollution, greenhouse gas emissions, human toxicity, and more.

Furthermore, a product with a **Health Product Declaration (HPD)** will provide disclosure about its material ingredients, a list of potential chemicals, related concerns, and additional health information.

For manufacturers or raw material suppliers, **Corporate Sustainability Reports (CSR)** will provide information about the manufacturer or raw material supplier of a product that has been verified to employ sustainable principles during the creation of their products.

By considering products with transparent information and declarations, project teams can make better decisions.

WASTE MANAGEMENT AND REDUCTION

The construction industry is responsible for the generation of huge amounts of waste. According to the EPA, in 1996, 136 million tons of construction and demolition debris were generated in the United States. In hindsight, it can be said that most of it could have been used in better ways.

Green building projects should work on reducing the amount of waste that goes to landfills. With the development and implementation of a **waste management plan** for both the construction and operation phases of a building, project teams can identify potential waste streams and also look for ways to reuse or recycle them. Below are some of the items that can be reused or recycled:

- Brick
- Metals
- Wood
- Carpet
- Wallboard
- Glass
- Plastic
- Cardboard
- Mixed paper
- Lighting accessories

At a minimum, all the LEED projects must recycle <u>paper</u>, <u>corrugated cardboard</u>, <u>glass</u>, <u>plastics,</u> and <u>metals</u> during the building operations phase; this will also be discussed under the "Storage and Collection of Recyclables" prerequisite.

According to the local recycling programs, projects may determine which materials will be stored separately and which may be commingled into a single stream, which is called **commingled recycling**. With commingled recycling, less space is needed to store items, and participation levels may increase since all items go into a single container without sorting.

The EPA developed a hierarchy, ranking the most environmentally sound strategies for reducing municipal solid waste:

1. Source reduction (the most important strategy)
2. Reuse
3. Recycle
4. Waste-to-energy conversion

The waste-to-energy strategy converts nonrecyclable materials into usable heat, electricity, or fuel through combustion, gasification, pyrolization, anaerobic digestion, and landfill gas recovery (LGR).

Following are some other strategies to address waste management and reduction:

- Establish a tracking system and ensure that the general contractor provides waste hauler reports and that the full scope of waste is captured
- Develop a solid waste management policy, which specifies target diversion rates for the facility

- Conduct a waste stream audit and identify opportunities for increased recycling, waste diversion, and occupant education
- Stress composting, which can include turning landscaping debris into mulch and working with the waste hauler for collection, composting of food, and other organic items
- Collect durable goods—which can include furniture, televisions, appliances, and office equipment—for donation, reuse, or recycling

SUSTAINABLE PURCHASING

Green buildings need to address sustainable purchasing during the building operations phase. Developing a **sustainable material purchasing program** can foster choosing environmentally friendly products when buying office papers, computers, furniture, light bulbs, and more.

Mercury, which is toxic, is present in many low-energy light bulbs, such as compact fluorescent lights (CFLs). If items similar to CFLs are used in a building, the facility manager should make sure these items do not go into the regular waste disposal process as the other items do. However, the best option would still be to purchase light bulbs free of mercury.

When purchasing sustainable cleaning products, the facility manager can look for green custodial products that meet the **Green Seal**, **Environmental Choice**, or **EPA standards** in order to protect the indoor air quality and also to reduce environmental damage.

The following third-party certifications can help identify sustainable products related to food:

- **Fairtrade**: Promotes sustainable principles in products such as coffee, tea, sugar, fruits, and chocolate
- **Food Alliance**: Certifies farms, ranches, and food handlers
- **USDA Organic**: Regulates the standards of agricultural products
- **Protected Harvest**: Certifies farmers' use of stringent environmental and sustainable growing standards
- **Marine Stewardship Council Blue Eco-Label**: Certifies sustainable fishing
- **Rainforest Alliance Certification**: Promotes sustainability in agriculture and forestry

STRATEGIES TO ADDRESS MATERIALS AND RESOURCES

- Reuse existing buildings and salvaged materials
- Plan for smaller, more compact communities
- Design smaller, more flexible homes and buildings
- Use efficient framing techniques
- Implement source reduction
- Conduct life-cycle assessment (LCA)
- Look for Cradle-to-Cradle certified products
- Look for products that are sustainably grown and harvested, are made from rapidly re-newable materials, are toxin free, are manufactured in factories that support human health and workers' rights, are long-lasting and reusable, contain recycled content, have intended end-of-life scenarios that avoid landfills, and are low in embodied energy
- Identify local sources of environmentally preferred products
- Develop a sustainable materials policy
- Specify green materials and equipment and look for third-party certifications like Green Seal, ENERGY STAR, or something similar
- Specify green custodial products that meet Green Seal, Environmental Choice, or EPA standards
- Avoid greenwashing and look for transparent products that contain an EPD and an HPD
- When choosing manufacturers or raw material suppliers, look for a CSR
- Develop a construction waste policy
- Develop a solid waste management policy
- Establish a waste tracking system
- Conduct a waste stream audit
- Maintain a recycling program
- Compost
- Provide recycling for durable goods such as e-waste and furniture
- Develop a sustainable purchasing program during the building operations phase

STORAGE AND COLLECTION OF RECYCLABLES—PREREQUISITE

PREREQUISITE SUMMARY

Waste is one of the primary burdens on the environment. In the United States, metals, paper, food, glass, and plastics comprise approximately 69% of the total amount of municipal solid waste.[2] Furthermore, all the mentioned products can be recycled, and recycling not only reduces the need for virgin materials, but it also reduces the need for landfills.

In addition to solid waste, electronic waste (e-waste) is a major problem in today's world since the disposal of these materials can cause more harm to the environment. But handling electronic waste requires different procedures.

This prerequisite aims to reduce the waste that is generated by <u>building occupants.</u> (Waste produced during the construction phase will be addressed by the next prerequisite; this prerequisite <u>only</u> addresses waste produced by the building users.) In turn, this prerequisite forces the project teams to have spaces dedicated to the collection and storage of recyclables, at least for mixed paper, corrugated cardboard, glass, plastics, and metals, all of which can be accessed by waste haulers and building occupants in the entire building.

Such projects should also be able to have an infrastructure in place to collect, store, and dispose of at least two of the following: batteries, lamps containing mercury, and electronic waste. Note that these materials are not considered recyclable items under this prerequisite, as they will be only collected, stored, and disposed of.

For the LEED BD+C Core and Shell projects, the recycling policy of a building should be defined in tenant lease agreements in order to ensure that tenants design their own spaces for recycling and storing materials.

PREREQUISITE INTENT

Reducing the waste generated by the building users and hauled to landfills.

PREREQUISITE REQUIREMENTS

Provide dedicated areas that can be accessible by the waste haulers and building occupants for the collection and storage of recyclable materials for the entire building. Collection and storage areas can be located separately as well. Recyclable materials must include **mixed paper, corrugated cardboard, glass, plastics,** and **metals**. Also, necessary actions need to be taken for safe collection, storage, and disposal of two of the following: **batteries, mercury-containing lamps,** and **electronic waste.**

KEY THINGS TO REMEMBER

- Batteries, mercury-containing lamps, and electronic waste are not recyclable materials under this prerequisite. They will be collected, stored, and disposed of.
- By this prerequisite, every LEED BD+C project should recycle at least mixed paper, corrugated cardboard, glass, plastics, and metals.
- This prerequisite is only for the building operations phase and not for the construction phase. And the next prerequisite is only for the construction phase and not for the building operations phase.

CONSTRUCTION AND DEMOLITION WASTE MANAGEMENT PLANNING— PREREQUISITE

PREREQUISITE SUMMARY

Construction waste is another waste category that makes up a significant portion of the total waste produced in the world. This prerequisite encourages the project teams to create a **construction and demolition waste management plan** to identify potential strategies for reducing the generated construction waste.

To achieve the prerequisite, the project should set goals for waste diversion by choosing at least five suitable materials to be diverted. At the end of construction, the project teams should prepare a final report showing the total construction waste generated and what portion of that waste was disposed of or diverted.

This prerequisite also has a credit called "Construction and Demolition Waste Management" that will be discussed at the end of this chapter. If the project teams choose to implement the construction and demolition waste management plan by meeting the target diversion rates defined in the credit, then the credit can be earned according to the succeeded diversion rates. In fact, this prerequisite does not force implementation of a developed waste management plan with the target diversion rates set forth by USGBC; rather, it only asks the project teams to create a plan, which includes their targets and a final report showing the total waste versus diverted and disposed of waste.

As discussed, the best technique to eliminate project waste is <u>source reduction</u>, which is accomplished by planning the materials to be produced at exact sizes through prefabrication, modular construction, or a similar method, so that no waste is generated on-site at all. The other waste reduction strategies can include reuse, recycling, donation, and salvage. For the generated waste, <u>source separation</u> can be accomplished by sorting the waste materials into recycling streams.

This prerequisite only addresses waste management during the <u>construction phase</u>, and therefore it does not cover the waste from the building occupants, unlike the previous prerequisite. In order not to confuse these prerequisites and credits, simply look at the title and see whether or not it contains the word "construction."

PREREQUISITE INTENT

By recycling, reusing, and recovering construction materials, the intent is to reduce the construction and demolition waste disposed of in landfills.

PREREQUISITE REQUIREMENTS

Develop and implement a construction and demolition waste management plan:

- Establish waste diversion goals by identifying at least five materials (both structural and nonstructural) targeted for diversion. Make an approximate calculation to show the percentage of these materials compared with total construction waste.
- Specify whether the materials are to be separated or commingled and explain the diversion strategies planned. Describe the transportation of the materials to the recycling facilities and describe the recycling process.

Write down a final report showing all major waste streams generated, including their disposal and diversion rates. Below is the formula to be used for disposal and diversion rate calculations:

Diversion rate = (Total waste diverted from landfill/Total waste produced by the project) x 100

It's important to note that **alternative daily cover (ADC)** does not qualify as a material diverted from disposal in LEED calculations. And **land-cleaning debris**, which is created by the removal of rock, soil, stone, and vegetation, is not considered waste since the ingredients are all natural products.

KEY THINGS TO REMEMBER

- This prerequisite is only for the construction phase, not for the building operations phase.
- Land cleaning debris and alternative daily cover (ADC) do not qualify as diverted materials in LEED calculations.

BUILDING LIFE CYCLE IMPACT REDUCTION—CREDIT

- 1–5 Points

CREDIT SUMMARY

This credit is about reducing the environmental impact that is created through the building's life cycle. Life-cycle assessment (LCA) comes as a great tool and is featured in option 4 of the credit. The projects that implement a whole-building life-cycle assessment will earn points under option 4.

Nevertheless, there is even a more effective way to reduce the environmental impact of a building, which is to reuse existing buildings/materials since it is not necessary to think about the environmental impacts of producing new materials when the existing material can be reused. And this credit's options 1, 2, and 3 each award more points than option 4, with the reuse of historic buildings, renovation of abandoned/blighted buildings, or building and material reuse.

CREDIT INTENT

Optimizing environmental performance and promoting adaptive reuse of materials and products.

CREDIT REQUIREMENTS

Demonstrate reduced environmental effects by reusing existing building resources or demonstrating a reduction in materials use through life-cycle assessment. Achieve one of the following options.

Option 1: Historic building reuse—5 points
Maintain the existing building structure, envelope, and interior nonstructural elements of a historic building or contributing building inside a historic district. To qualify, the building or historic district must be listed or eligible for listing in the local, state, or national register of historic places. Do not demolish any part of a historic building or contributing building in a historic district unless it has structural problems or contains hazardous materials.

OR

Option 2: Renovation of abandoned or blighted building—5 points

Maintain at least **50%**, by <u>surface area</u>, of the existing building structure, enclosure, and interior structural elements in buildings which meet local criteria of abandoned or are considered blight. The building then must be renovated to a state of productive occupancy. If there is any deterioration or damage, up to **25%** of the building surface area may be excluded from credit calculation.

OR

Option 3: Building and material reuse—2–4 points

Reuse or salvage building materials from off-site or on-site locations, and calculate the reuse or salvage as a percentage of the project's <u>surface area</u>. Points will be awarded according as listed in table 20. Structural elements (e.g., floors or roof decking), enclosure materials (e.g., skin or framing), and permanently installed interior elements (e.g., walls, doors, floor coverings, or ceiling systems) are included. Window assemblies and any hazardous materials that are remediated as a part of the project are excluded from the calculations.

Materials contributing toward this credit cannot contribute toward the "Building Product Disclosure and Optimization—Sourcing of Raw Materials" credit.

% of completed project surface area reused	Points
25%	2
50%	3
75%	4

Table 20

OR

Option 4: Whole-building life-cycle assessment—3 points

For new construction (buildings or portions of buildings), conduct a life-cycle assessment of the project's structure and enclosure. The assessment should demonstrate a minimum of 10% reduction compared with a baseline building. Reductions should be in at least three of the six impact categories listed below, <u>one of</u> which must be <u>global warming potential</u>. No impact category evaluated as part of the life-cycle assessment may increase by more than 5% compared with the baseline building.

The building should fully account for maintenance and replacement for at least 60 years. And for this calculation, data sets must be compliant with ISO 14044.

Select at least three of the following impact categories for reduction, (one of them should be the global warming potential):

- Global warming potential (greenhouse gases) in CO_2e;
- Depletion of the stratospheric ozone layer, in kilograms (kg) of CFC-11;
- Acidification of land and water sources, in moles of H+ or kg of SO_2;
- Eutrophication, in kg of nitrogen or kg of phosphate;
- Formation of tropospheric ozone, in kg of NOx, kg of O_3 eq, or kg of ethene
- Depletion of nonrenewable energy resources, in MJ.

KEY THINGS TO REMEMBER

- The impact categories used for whole-building life-cycle assessment in option 4.
- Global warming is the top priority of LEED. This is the reason that the life-cycle assessment (LCA) reductions should be made in at least three of the six impact categories listed above, and <u>one of those must be tied to global warming potential</u>.

BUILDING PRODUCT DISCLOSURE AND OPTIMIZATION: ENVIRONMENTAL PRODUCT DECLARATION

- 1–2 Points

CREDIT SUMMARY

This credit encourages the use of **permanently installed products and materials** with preferred life-cycle impacts. Environmental Product Declarations (EPD) show a product's raw material extraction effects to the environment, energy use, chemical makeup, waste generation, and any emissions made to water, air, and soil during the entire sourcing and manufacturing process. Supporting the use of products with EPDs will increase the number of environmentally friendly manufacturers. However, the credit only accepts EPDs that conform to ISO standards.

Option 1 of the credit requires the use of permanently installed products manufactured by the companies that provide EPDs for their products. Projects should use at least 20 different permanently installed products sourced from at least five different manufacturers that also meet the requirements of option 1. However, all product EPDs are not equally weighted with regard to the credit-achievement calculations, as will be discussed under the credit requirements. For example, a product with an industry-wide (generic) EPD will be counted as a half (1/2) product, while a product with a product-specific Type III EPD will be counted as one whole (1) product. And according to the valuation criteria, the sum of the products should add up to 20.

Option 2, which refers to multiattribute optimization, requires the use of third-party-certified, permanently installed products that are proven to have less environmental impact than the regular products in at least 3 of the 6 impact categories. The applicable impact categories are the global warming potential, the depletion of the stratospheric ozone layer, the acidification of land and water sources, eutrophication, the formation of tropospheric ozone, and the depletion of nonrenewable energy resources.

In order to show compliance with this credit's option 2, the project teams need to calculate the cost of materials in compliance with the option 2 requirements and multiply their cost by a valuation factor to show that **50%** of all the permanently installed building products have preferred life-cycle impacts. For example, a product with a global warming potential, eutrophication, and a formation of tropospheric ozone values below the industry average, according to third party certification will be valued at 100% of its cost. However, if that product is sourced (extracted, manufactured, and purchased) within **100 miles** (160 km) (which is the location valuation factor of LEED) of the project site, the product will be valued at **200%** of its cost.

CREDIT INTENT

Encouraging the use of products and materials that contain life-cycle information and have environmentally, socially, and economically preferred life-cycle impacts. And awarding the project teams are awarded for choosing manufacturers that have verified, improved environmental life-cycle impacts.

CREDIT REQUIREMENTS

Achieve one or more of the options below, for a maximum of 2 points.

Option 1: Environmental product declaration (EPD)—1 point
Use at least 20 different permanently installed products, sourced from at least five different manufacturers that meet one of the disclosure criteria below.

- Product-specific declaration: Products with a publicly available, critically reviewed life-cycle assessment conforming to **ISO 14044** that have at least a cradle-to-gate scope assessment. As mentioned, cradle-to-gate assessment is the product assessment between the sourcing of the raw materials and the finished product at the factory gate ready for sale. These products will be valued as one-quarter of a product for the purposes of credit-achievement calculations.

- Environmental Product Declarations that conform to ISO 14025, 14040, 14044, and EN 15804 or ISO 21930 and have at least a cradle-to-gate scope.

    a. Products with industry-wide (generic) EPD: These products will be valued as one half (1/2) of a product for the purposes of credit-achievement calculations.

    b. Products with product-specific Type III EPD: These products will be valued as one whole product (1) for the purposes of credit-achievement calculations.

- Other USGBC-approved program—Products that comply with other USGBC-approved environmental product declaration frameworks.

AND/OR

Option 2: Multiattribute optimization—1 point
Fifty percent, **by cost**, of the permanently installed products used in the project should comply with one of the following criteria:

➤ Third-party-certified products that demonstrate impact reduction below the industry average **in at least three** of the following impact categories are valued at **100%** of their cost for credit-achievement calculations:

    a. Global warming potential (greenhouse gases), in CO_2e

    c. Depletion of the stratospheric ozone layer, in kilograms (kg) of CFC-11

    d. Acidification of land and water sources, in moles of H+ or kg of SO_2

    e. Eutrophication, in kg of nitrogen or kg of phosphate

    f. Formation of tropospheric ozone, in kg of NOx, kg of O_3 eq, or kg of thane

    g. Depletion of nonrenewable energy resources, in MJ

➤ Other USGBC-approved programs—Products that comply with other USGBC-approved multiattribute frameworks.

For credit-achievement calculations, products that are sourced (extracted, manufactured, and purchased) within **100 miles** (160 km) of the project site will be valued at **200%** of their base contributing cost.

Structure and enclosure materials cannot constitute more than 30% of the value of compliant building products.

KEY THINGS TO REMEMBER

◼ For credit-achievement calculations under option 2, products sourced within 100 miles (160 km) of the project site are valued at **200%** of their base contributing cost, which is the location valuation factor of LEED.

◼ The names of the impact categories defined in this credit's option 2.

BUILDING PRODUCT DISCLOSURE AND OPTIMIZATION: SOURCING OF RAW MATERIALS—CREDIT

- 1–2 Points

CREDIT SUMMARY

The principles employed during the raw material extraction process are very important for reducing the environmental impacts resulting from the creation of a product. Think about a wood supplier that cuts trees without planting any new ones. This approach can only result in a loss of habitat and deforestation.

In order to prevent similar environmental impacts, option 1 of this credit (raw material source and extraction reporting) encourages the use of products that are sourced from ecologically responsible raw material suppliers. The raw material suppliers with third-party-verified corporate sustainability reports (CSR) and self-declared reports should be chosen by project teams in order to encourage sustainable raw material source and extraction principles.

In this credit's option 2, leadership extraction practices promote the use of materials that are <u>biobased</u>, **Forest Stewardship Council (FSC)**-certified, reused, have recycled content (<u>postconsumer</u> and <u>preconsumer recycled content</u>), or contain a producer-responsibility program.

The Forest Stewardship Council is a voluntary program that sets standards for wood product manufacturers to ensure responsible forest management in order to prevent deforestation and loss of habitat. The FSC provides a **chain of custody (CoC)** certification, which is a procedure that tracks a product from the point of harvest/extraction to its distribution.

Preconsumer recycled content is the content of a material that is recycled before being used by a consumer. An example of this could be sawdust generated during the manufacturing of a wood product. The by-product (sawdust) is then recycled, in order to be used inside an MDF board (medium-density fiberboard). Thus, the sawdust was never consumed by anyone, and it was directly recycled into a totally different product. Other types of materials with preconsumer recycled content can be <u>wood chips</u>, <u>tree bark</u>, <u>magazine overruns</u>, and <u>a number of supplemental cementitious materials (SCMs),</u> such as <u>fly ash</u>.

Postconsumer recycled content is the recycled content of a used material. For example, recyclable printer paper can be sent to be recycled after being used and can then become a part of a new printer paper. Other types of materials with postconsumer recycled content can be <u>aluminum cans</u>, <u>water bottles</u>, most types of <u>glass</u>, <u>wood</u> and <u>steel products</u>, <u>newspapers,</u> and many others.

Extended Producer Responsibility (EPR) is a product stewardship policy approach that holds consumer goods companies responsible for managing their own products and packaging when consumers are finished with them.

Lastly, **biobased materials** are products other than food that are biological products, renewable agricultural materials, or forestry materials. Biobased materials are derived from biomass. Plants and animals can be examples of biobased materials; however, <u>hide products</u>, such as leather and other animal skin material, are <u>excluded in LEED calculations</u>.

As in the previous "BDPO—Environmental Product Declarations" credit, project teams need to do some credit-achievement calculations in order to show compliance with the credit. And again, the valuation factors will be different for each of the criteria in the credit's requirements.

CREDIT INTENT

Encouraging the use of products and materials that have life-cycle information and have environmentally, socially, and economically preferred life-cycle impacts. Awarding project teams for choosing products that have been verified as sourced or extracted in a responsible manner.

CREDIT REQUIREMENTS

Option 1: Raw material source and extraction reporting—1 point

Use at least 20 permanently installed building materials, from at least five different manufacturers, that have publicly released a report that shows raw material extraction locations, commitment to ecologically responsible land use, commitment to meeting applicable standards, and commitment to reducing environmental harm during extraction.

- Products sourced from manufacturers with self-declared reports are valued as one-half of a product (1/2) for credit-achievement calculation.
- Products with third-party-verified corporate sustainability reports (CSR) are valued as one whole product (1) for credit-achievement calculation. Acceptable CSRs include:

    a. Global Reporting Initiative (GRI) Sustainability Report
    b. Organization for Economic Cooperation and Development (OECD) Guidelines for Multinational Enterprises
    c. UN Global Compact: Communication of Progress
    d. ISO 26000: 2010 Guidance on Social Responsibility
    e. Other USGBC-approved programs

AND/OR

Option 2: Leadership extraction practices—1 point

Use products that meet at least one of the responsible extraction criteria below for at least 25% of the total <u>cost</u> of permanently installed building products in the project.

- **Extended producer responsibility (EPR):** Products purchased from a manufacturer that are involved in an extended producer responsibility program. Products meeting this criterion are valued at **50%** of their cost in the credit-achievement calculation.

- **Biobased materials:** Biobased products that meet the Sustainable Agriculture Network's Sustainable Agriculture Standard. Biobased raw materials must be tested using ASTM Test Method D6866. **Hide products,** such as leather and other animal skin material, are <u>excluded</u>. Products meeting biobased material criteria are valued at **100%** of their cost in the credit-achievement calculation.

- **Wood products:** Wood products must be certified by the **Forest Stewardship Council (FSC).** Products meeting wood products criteria are valued at **100%** of their cost in the credit-achievement calculation.

- **Materials reuse:** This criterion includes salvaged, refurbished, or reused products. Products meeting reuse criteria are valued at **100%** of their cost in the credit-achievement calculation.

- **Recycled content:** Recycled content is the sum of postconsumer recycled content plus one-half the preconsumer recycled content, which is based on cost. Products meeting wood products criteria are valued at 100% of their cost in the credit-achievement calculation.

- **Other USGBC-approved program**

For credit-achievement calculation, materials sourced (extracted, manufactured, and purchased) within **100 miles** (160 km) (which is the location valuation factor of LEED) of the project site are valued at **200%** of their cost.

KEY THINGS TO REMEMBER

- Definitions of postconsumer recycled content and preconsumer recycled content.
- Examples of items with postconsumer recycled content and preconsumer recycled content.
- Forest Stewardship Council (FSC), a very important organization to know for exam purposes
- Definition of chain of custody.
- Materials sourced (extracted, manufactured and purchased) within **100 miles** (160 km) of the project site and valued at **200%** of their cost, which is the location valuation factor of LEED.
- Recycled content is the sum of postconsumer recycled content plus one-half the preconsumer recycled content, which is based on cost.
- Purpose of corporate sustainability reports (CSR).
- Definition of biobased material, biobased material types, and exclusions.

BUILDING PRODUCT DISCLOSURE AND OPTIMIZATION (BPDO): MATERIAL INGREDIENTS—CREDIT

- 1–2 Points

CREDIT SUMMARY

In the United States, 96% of the 85,000 building products have not been screened for possible health effects.[3] The use of persistent bioaccumulative and toxic chemicals (PBTs) and persistent organic pollutants (POPs) are mostly found in building products, which cause serious harm to organisms and can even affect the health of animals and plants living miles away.

This credit encourages the use of products that have been screened for their chemical ingredients, and it aims to transform the market so that producers pay more attention to chemical screenings.

Green chemistry is the design of chemical products and processes that eliminate the use and generation of hazardous substances.[4] Therefore, it should be implemented for all products. Manufacturers should disclose information about the ingredients in their products so that consumers can make better decisions when choosing environmentally friendly products.

Cradle-to-Cradle Certification (C$_2$C), GreenScreen, and **REACH Optimization** are also mentioned in the credit, in which the Cradle-to-Cradle Certification (C$_2$C) assesses the ingredients of a product for environmental and human health hazards and awards a Basic, Bronze, Silver, Gold, or Platinum level Cradle-to-Cradle Certification to the products with preferable life-cycle impacts.

GreenScreen is a method used to identify chemicals of high concern and also to identify safer alternatives. GreenScreen is developed by Clean Production Action, a nonprofit organization.

The acronym in REACH Optimization stands for Registration, Evaluation, Authorization, and Restriction of Chemicals. It is the outgrowth of European Union legislation that requires all chemicals sold to be evaluated based on their hazard profiles. Only projects outside the United States can use REACH Optimization as an alternative compliance path (ACP).

As with the previous "BDPO" credits, project teams need to do some credit-achievement calculations in order to show compliance with the credit, and the valuation factors will be different for each criterion in the credit's requirements.

CREDIT INTENT

Encouraging the use of products and materials that have life-cycle information and have environmentally, socially, and economically preferred life-cycle impacts. Promoting project teams for choosing products with chemical ingredients that are inventoried according to the accepted methodologies and are verified to minimize the use of harmful substances. Also promoting raw material manufacturers that provides improved life-cycle impact products.

CREDIT REQUIREMENTS

Option 1: Material ingredient reporting—1 point
Use at least 20 different permanently installed building products, from at least five different manufacturers, that have published reports about the chemical inventory of the material (to at least 0.1%) by the use of any of the following programs:

- **Manufacturer Inventory:** The manufacturer should have published the complete content of the product by showing all the ingredients by name and the Chemical Abstract Service Registration Number (CASRN). Materials that are defined as trade secrets may not show the name and/or CASRN, but they should still disclose the role, amount, and GreenScreen benchmark under GreenScreen v1.2.
- **Health Product Declaration**
- **Cradle-to-cradle Certified (C_2C):** Cradle-to-Cradle v2 Basic level or Cradle-to-Cradle v3 Bronze level
- **Other USGBC-approved programs**

AND/OR

Option 2: Material ingredient optimization—1 point
Use materials that have published reports through one of the following programs, for at least 25% of the cost of the total value of permanently installed materials:

- GreenScreen v1.2 Benchmark:

   a. If any ingredients are assessed with the GreenScreen List Translator, value the product at 100% of its cost.
   b. If all ingredients have undergone a full GreenScreen Assessment, value the product at 150% of its cost.

- Cradle-to-Cradle Certified:

    a. Cradle-to-Cradle v2 Gold, value the product at 100% of its cost
    b. Cradle-to-Cradle v2 Platinum, value the product at 150% of its cost
    c. Cradle-to-Cradle v3 Silver, value the product at 100% of its cost
    d. Cradle-to-Cradle v3 Gold or Platinum, value the product at 150% of its cost

- International Alternative Compliance Path—REACH Optimization: Use products that do not contain substances that meet REACH criteria for substances of very high concern. If the product doesn't contain any ingredients listed on the REACH Authorization or Candidate list, value the product at 100% of its cost in the credit calculations.
- Other USGBC-approved program

AND/OR

Option 3: Product Manufacturer Supply Chain Optimization—1 point
Use materials that have published reports to document their safety and health practices throughout the supply chain—for at least 25% of the cost of the total value of permanently installed materials that have the following characteristics:

- Are sourced from product manufacturers who engage in validated and robust safety, health, hazard, and risk programs.
- Are sourced from product manufacturers having independent third-party verification of their supply chain, which verifies health, safety, and environmental processes. Products that meet this option will be valued at 100% of their cost in the credit calculations.

For both options 2 and 3, products that are sourced (extracted, manufactured and purchased) within **100 miles** (160 km) of the project site are valued at **200%** of their cost.

KEY THINGS TO REMEMBER

- Definition of green chemistry.
- GreenScreen.
- Cradle-to-Cradle Certification.
- REACH Optimization.

CONSTRUCTION AND DEMOLITION WASTE MANAGEMENT—CREDIT

- 1–2 Points

CREDIT SUMMARY

This is the credit of the "Construction and Demolition Waste Management Planning" prerequisite. If the project teams implement their construction and demolition waste management plans, as developed in the prerequisite, and also reach the diversion thresholds specified in this credit, they will earn the credit.

In the prerequisite, project teams set the diversion rates, so implementing the construction and demolition waste management plan was optional. But the diversion rates in this credit are set by the USGBC, and implementing the plan is required to earn the credit.

CREDIT INTENT

By recycling, reusing, and recovering construction materials, the intent is to reduce the construction and demolition waste disposed of in landfills.

CREDIT REQUIREMENTS

Recycle and/or salvage nonhazardous construction and demolition materials. Calculations can be by weight or volume but should be consistent throughout.

Excavated soil, land-clearing debris, alternative daily cover (ADC), and hazardous materials should be excluded from the calculations. Wood waste that is converted to fuel (biofuel) can be included in the credit calculations. Other types of waste-to-energy production (other than wood waste) should be excluded.

However, for projects that cannot meet credit requirements using "reuse" and "recycling" methods, waste-to-energy systems may be considered waste diversion if the European Commission Waste Framework Directive 2008/98/EC and Waste Incineration Directive 2000/76/EC are followed, and Waste to Energy facilities must meet applicable European Committee for Standardization (CEN) EN 303 standards.

Option 1: Diversion—1–2 points

Path 1: Divert 50% and three material streams—1 point
Divert at least 50% of the total construction and demolition material. Diverted materials should include at least three material streams.

OR

Path 2: Divert 75% and four material streams—2 points
Divert at least 75% of the total construction and demolition material. Diverted materials should include at least four material streams.

OR

Option 2: Reduction of total waste material—2 points
Do not generate more than 2.5 pounds of construction waste per square foot (12.2 kilograms of waste per square meter) of the building's floor area.

KEY THINGS TO REMEMBER

- Excavated soil, land-clearing debris, alternative daily cover (ADC), and hazardous materials are always excluded from LEED diversion calculations.
- Wood waste, which is converted to fuel (biofuel), is included in LEED diversion calculations.

CHAPTER 10

INDOOR ENVIRONMENTAL QUALITY (EQ)

This credit category is about the strategies related to indoor air quality and thermal, visual, and acoustic comfort. A good standard of indoor environmental quality is essential in green buildings to protect the health and comfort of building occupants. Moreover, thermal, visual, and acoustic qualities of a building are important in increasing occupants' comfort level and productivity.

This chapter will discuss both the importance of indoor environmental quality for the building occupants and construction workers and its effects on the green building design. After discussing the EQ credit category, the book will go over all the EQ prerequisites and credits individually to show how these features are used in LEED certification for a LEED BD+C: New Construction and Major Renovation project.

The EQ credit category will be discussed under two major sections:

- Indoor air quality
- Increased occupant comfort

INDOOR AIR QUALITY

In order to increase the indoor air quality of a building, first, the sources of contaminants should be identified, and necessary measures should be taken to prevent them from reaching the indoors, which is also called **source control.**

Below are some of the contaminants that will negatively affect the indoor air quality of a building:

- Tobacco smoke
- Building materials with high levels of volatile organic compounds (VOCs)
- Mold growth
- Cleaning products
- Construction contamination of building materials
- Combustion process in the HVAC equipment
- Radon or methane off-gassing from the building's located soil
- Pollutants in the occupants' shoes
- Pollutants from specific processes used in hospitals, laboratories, and factories

Studies show that poor indoor air quality can result in respiratory disease, allergies, asthma, and sick building syndrome (SBS) or other building-related illnesses (BRI).

In order to avoid poor indoor air quality, a project should do the following:

- Set minimum air quality standards
- Stop secondhand smoke
- Use low-emitting materials
- Protect the site during construction
- Schedule construction activities to minimize occupant exposure
- Increase ventilation rates
- Monitor carbon dioxide
- Implement green cleaning practices
- Periodically maintain and replace air filters
- Reduce radon levels

To take the discussion to the next level, let's discuss these strategies individually.

SET MINIMUM AIR QUALITY STANDARDS

All LEED BD+C projects must comply with certain aspects of the ASHRAE 62.1 standard (which is a ventilation standard used to achieve acceptable indoor air quality) or the local codes as part of the "Minimum Air Quality Performance" prerequisite.

After the minimum air quality standards have been set, monitoring the indoor air quality is essential since, in some cases, providing sufficient amounts of fresh air to the building may not be enough. If a project is located in a city with high air pollution, the filtration level of the supply air may need to be increased, and the air can be further tested to ensure high indoor air quality.

STOP SECONDHAND SMOKE

Exposure to secondhand smoke can cause lung cancer in nonsmokers and also increase the risk of heart disease.

Any school project that aims for a LEED certification should prohibit smoking on the entire campus, both indoors and outdoors.

For other project types, LEED prohibits smoking indoors and does not allow smoking within 25 feet of the building entrance.

For residential projects, LEED requires partitioning of the rooms and also prohibits smoking in the common spaces. Additionally, it requires a blower door test to ensure that air cannot leak from smoking units to others.

Smoking requirements will be addressed under the "Environmental Tobacco Smoke Control" prerequisite.

USE LOW-EMITTING MATERIALS

Material off-gassing can seriously affect indoor air quality and human health. The amount of **volatile organic compounds (VOCs)**, such as **formaldehyde**, contained in construction materials will affect the health of both the construction workers and the building occupants.

Many building materials, such as adhesives, sealants, composite wood, paints, coatings, floorings, furniture, wall coverings, and other products such as photocopy machines can contain harmful levels of VOCs.

LEED addresses VOC and other requirements regarding material off-gassing under the "Low-Emitting Materials" credit, and in order to earn the credit, projects need to follow the VOC thresholds set for each item category.

Using building products that meet the third-party standards for their emitting potential is also encouraged by LEED. Table 21 shows the third parties and their associated product types, which are also important to know for exam purposes.

Referenced LEED Standard	Product Type
South Coast Air Quality Management District (SCAQMD)	Adhesives, sealants, primers, floor coatings, wood finishes
Green Seal	Paints and coatings, anticorrosive and antirust paints, aerosol adhesives
Green Label (Carpet and Rug Institute)	Carpets
Green Label Plus (Carpet and Rug Institute)	Carpet cushion
GREENGUARD	Furniture and seating
FloorScore	Vinyl, linoleum, wood, ceramic, laminate, and rubber flooring

Table 21

Naturally occurring materials and products made from inorganic materials such as marble or granite contain low or no VOCs and are therefore exempt from LEED requirements. These materials are called **inherently nonemitting materials**.

PROTECT THE SITE DURING CONSTRUCTION

The project team should develop and implement an indoor air quality (IAQ) plan in order to protect the health of both the construction workers and the building occupants. While developing the IAQ plan, the project team can refer to the **Sheet Metal and Air Conditioning National Contractors Association (SMACNA)** guidelines, which describe the necessary control measures to be taken during the construction phase to maintain sufficient indoor air quality.

Think about the HVAC ducts stored on-site without any protection and collecting all the dust before getting installed; even if the building has increased its ventilation rates, all the air that will be supplied by the ducts will be contaminated air, which will decrease the indoor air quality as a consequence.

To ensure compliance, LEED requires proper site protection during the construction phase by requiring project teams to take and send site photos to document their actions.

SCHEDULE CONSTRUCTION ACTIVITIES TO MINIMIZE OCCUPANT EXPOSURE

After the completion of construction, the project team should make sure that any contamination and dust are cleared before the building occupants arrive. To ensure sufficient air quality after the completion of construction, an **air quality test** can be conducted.

Or the project team can choose to conduct a **flush-out**, which is a process of supplying ample amounts of fresh air to the building before or during occupancy; this process will take away the contaminated air and establish the desired level of indoor air quality.

INCREASE VENTILATION RATES

Fresh air is by far the most important element of indoor air quality, and supplying ample amounts of fresh air inside the building will strongly affect the indoor air quality. This can be established by increasing the ventilation rates of the HVAC system; however, this will also increase the energy consumption and operating costs of the building. Increased ventilation will result in lowering the ratio of poor air and increase the removal of indoor contaminants.

Otherwise, if the climate in the project location is appropriate, **natural ventilation** can be established by the opening of windows and doors, which would also reduce the building operating costs.

In an appropriate climate, projects can use **mixed-mode ventilation,** which employs both HVAC and natural ventilation.

MONITOR CARBON DIOXIDE (CO$_2$)

An effective way to ensure good indoor air quality is to monitor the carbon dioxide levels inside the building. By installing carbon dioxide monitoring equipment, the thresholds for CO$_2$ levels can be determined, and once CO$_2$ levels increase above the threshold, necessary actions can be taken to increase the amount of fresh air inside the building.

IMPLEMENT GREEN CLEANING PRACTICES

Using green cleaning products will have a lower detrimental impact than regular cleaning products. A **green cleaning program** can be developed that specifies the green building products to be used (products can meet Green Seal, Environmental Choice, or EPA standards); the chemicals allowed to be used inside the building; the training of the cleaning personnel for the use of chemicals and green cleaning practices; indoor pest control plans; and energy-efficient cleaning equipment.

Additionally, installing cleanable entryway grates, grilles, or mats at every building entrance can keep the dirt, water, and contamination from shoes away from the building. These strategies will increase the indoor air quality while also reducing the amount of cleaning chemicals used in the building.

For the cleanliness of the building, **custodial effectiveness assessments** should also be conducted to obtain the occupants' opinions of the green cleaning program and to see whether they are ever exposed to contaminants.

PERIODICALLY MAINTAIN AND REPLACE AIR FILTERS

Without quality air filtration media, no building can establish good indoor air quality. The **minimum efficiency reporting value (MERV)** is an important term to know; which rates the air filters according to their success in removing particles from the air.

Air filters with higher MERV values will remove more particles from the air, but more energy will be consumed in passing the air through them. By keeping dust away from HVAC equipment, quality air filters will also increase the performance of the equipment.

To avoid clogged filters, frequent maintenance and replacement of air filters is necessary. Clogged filters will slow the velocity of air inside the ducts, cause molds, and also increase energy consumption of the HVAC equipment.

REDUCE RADON LEVELS

Radon is a radioactive gas that is naturally found in soils, rocks, and water bodies. Although we cannot see, smell, or taste radon, it can be detected with special equipment. If radon is found in a building, it is a serious problem that requires urgent action.

The presence of radon inside a building can create serious health effects such as lung cancer. The LEED for Homes rating system has a credit to address radon; the credit implements strategies to reduce radon infiltration into a residence.

Radon can infiltrate a building through the following:
- Cracks in solid floors
- Cracks in walls
- Construction joints
- Gaps in suspended floors
- Gaps around service pipes
- Water supply
- Cavities inside walls

INCREASE OCCUPANT COMFORT

Building occupants need to feel comfortable and in control of their environment in order to be healthy, happy, and productive in their buildings. There are several factors that will affect the comfort of an occupant. These include the following:

- Thermal comfort
- Daylighting
- Views
- Acoustics
- Lighting controls
- Temperature controls
- Ergonomics

However, merely addressing these factors will not be enough. **Occupant surveys** are also essential to ensure occupant comfort. By receiving occupant feedback, the building management can pinpoint areas that need to be improved.

THERMAL COMFORT

Thermal comfort is much more than merely adjusting the room temperature. It includes air movement and humidity as well. An occupant cannot feel comfortable under an HVAC duct that blows directly on him or her or if the unit does not provide even temperatures in all spaces.

All the LEED requirements about thermal comfort will be discussed under the "Thermal Comfort" credit.

DAYLIGHTING

Daylighting, a very important resource to use in green buildings, will increase the occupants' health, comfort, and productivity while also reducing building operating costs by using less artificial lighting inside the building. While too much daylighting can create discomfort, through means such as glare or direct sunlight to the occupant, an effective lighting design can overcome these consequences.

Increased cooling loads resulting from the heat of daylighting may be another consequence to be addressed by the project team. Using more technical skylights may allow only the sunlight to enter a building rather than additional heat.

The orientation of the building, configuration, the glass types for the windows, the layout of the rooms, the types of furnishings, and the colors of surfaces should all be considered during the design to maximize the use of daylighting without creating any discomfort. Spaces that are designed to efficiently use daylighting as their primary lighting source are called **daylit** spaces.

Below are some benefits of daylighting:

- Positive mental and physical effects on the building occupants
- Increased occupant productivity and comfort
- Cost savings due to the decreased usage of artificial lighting
- Cost savings due to increased occupant productivity

DAYLIGHTING SYSTEMS AND DESIGN

Daylighting systems can be categorized as either passive or active. **Passive daylighting** is a system that collects the sunlight using static and nonmoving items such as windows, glass doors, some skylights, light tubes, and light shelves. **Active daylighting** is a system that tracks and collects the sunlight using mechanical devices; however, these equipments may not function well on cloudy days.

Skylights are horizontal elements in the roof of a building that are made of opaque materials (mostly glass) to allow sunlight into the building. They can be thought of as the horizontal windows on the roof.

Light tubes, also called sun tubes or sun pipes, are structures that are used to transport sunlight inside a building. To illustrate, imagine a big pipe with a reflective inside surface that goes through the roof to the ceiling of a room. It captures the sunlight on the roof and transports it inside the pipe all the way down to the room.

Light shelves are horizontal, light-reflecting overhangs that are positioned to reflect the daylight into the desired area of the building.

Use of clerestory windows and appropriately sizing and locating all of the windows are important for increasing the amount of daylight introduced into a space. For office buildings, locating private offices toward the building's core and locating cubicles around the perimeter of the building can be effective strategies to bring daylight into a large area. Using **low cubicle partitions** will allow daylight into the core spaces and provide views to the outdoors.

Figure 12. Use of clerestory windows (courtesy of Guillaume Piolle)

To control glare and avoid direct sunlight reaching a building occupant, adjustable window shades can give occupants control over excessive brightness and glare. The project team should also evaluate the ground surfaces, adjacent buildings, pavement, and objects, as they all can cause glare.

Installing daylight controls is essential in reducing lighting costs. Lighting controls can dim or turn off the electrical lights completely when daylighting is sufficient. Zoning these controls is necessary since the spaces near the windows will have lots of natural light; thus, they can have dimmed artificial lighting. And the spaces away from the perimeter with less daylight can have higher levels of artificial light.

VIEWS

Having quality views in a building is another factor that will increase an occupant's comfort and productivity. Even if the building is in a great location that can provide wonderful views, the design of the building should maximize the use of those views to the building occupants.

Following are some design strategies to maximize the views:

- Using **vision glazing** (a term used for windows that provide exterior views)
- Using glazing without frits, patterns, colors, fibers, or tints
- Using low cubicle partitions or no partitions in open offices
- Adjusting building orientation, site design, facade, and interior layout to maximize views
- For office buildings, locating the private offices closer to the core of the building
- Removal of objects that obstruct views

It is also important to note that design strategies that provide quality views will also assist in increasing the daylighting inside a building; as some strategies are used for both.

ACOUSTICS

Building acoustics are an important part of the green building design that will affect an occupant's health, comfort, communication, and productivity. Students in schools can easily be disturbed by outside noise, as well as people working in open office environments. Hospital patients can have even more problems and privacy issues related to poor acoustics.

The LEED BD+C: Schools rating system contains a "Minimum Acoustic Performance" prerequisite that requires that all LEED-certified schools must implement an effective acoustic design. Further, all the LEED BD+C rating systems contain the "Acoustic Performance" credit, which awards projects for taking measures to improve the acoustic performance of a building. Acoustics will also be discussed in greater detail in the following pages.

LIGHTING CONTROLS

Providing individual lighting controls with adjustable lighting levels will increase occupant comfort and reduce lighting costs. If a big office space does not contain any individual lighting controls, all the lights should be "on," even if there are few people working in the office. Additionally, installing **occupancy sensors** will shut off light when an occupant is away from his or her desk and also reduce lighting usage.

A major aspect of lighting that will affect occupant comfort is lighting quality. The layout and intensity of lighting fixtures should be thoroughly evaluated during the design. Excess brightness and glare are factors that will cause discomfort to building users.

Installing **task lighting** is another important tool that will allow a user to illuminate an area for a specific task.

TEMPERATURE CONTROLS

Every individual has different temperature preferences. A certain temperature in an office building can make some people happy while other people can try to warm themselves up by putting on their sweaters or jackets.

Providing thermal comfort controls for individual spaces can allow building users to set their desired space temperature. Even though this strategy may not work in open offices, installing radiating heat panels under the desks can solve the problem.

ERGONOMICS

Office layouts, individual workstation design, furnishings, and equipment all contribute to the ergonomics of a building. Since every individual has different needs, the project team should consult and analyze occupant needs. Worker education and training should also be provided upon installation of furniture and equipment. Key ergonomic principles to be implemented should include flexibility, versatility, fit, and postural change.

STRATEGIES TO ADDRESS INDOOR ENVIRONMENTAL QUALITY

- Set minimum air quality standards
- Increase ventilation rates
- Protect the air that comes into the building
- Prohibit smoking
- Specify low-emitting materials
- Develop and follow a construction indoor air quality management plan
- Test for radon or other contaminants
- Use air filters with high MERV ratings
- Protect the site and building elements during construction
- Protect the air during construction
- Conduct a flush-out
- Conduct air testing after the construction to ensure good air quality
- Install entryway systems like grates, grilles, or mats to stop contaminants entering the building
- Monitor outdoor airflow and carbon dioxide
- Calibrate sensors as routine preventive maintenance
- Develop and implement a green cleaning policy
- Conduct custodial effectiveness assessment
- Use integrated pest management
- Use daylighting
- Maximize occupant views
- Install operable windows
- Provide temperature and ventilation controls to the occupants
- Provide lighting controls to the occupants
- Conduct occupant surveys
- Provide ergonomic features
- Address acoustics

MINIMUM INDOOR AIR QUALITY PERFORMANCE—PREREQUISITE

PREREQUISITE SUMMARY

Most of us predominantly spend our time inside buildings, breathing the air coming from the HVAC systems without being able to breathe fresh outside air. The ventilation rates of the HVAC systems and the contamination inside the ducts are important factors to consider, which may cause serious health effects. Properly ventilated spaces always contain fewer contaminants than poorly ventilated areas.

This prerequisite encourages project teams to design the building to maintain enough fresh air for the building occupants. This will happen by implementing strict indoor air quality standards for both ventilation and air monitoring. For LEED BD+C Core and Shell projects, the tenants should design their spaces according to these requirements as well.

PREREQUISITE INTENT

Committing to the well-being and comfort of building occupants by setting minimum standards for indoor air quality (IAQ).

PREREQUISITE REQUIREMENTS

Meet the requirements for both <u>ventilation</u> and <u>monitoring</u>.

Ventilation

Mechanically ventilated spaces
For mechanically ventilated spaces (and for mixed-mode systems when the mechanical ventilation is activated):

Option 1: ASHRAE Standard 62.1-2010
Meet the minimum requirements of ASHRAE Standard 62.1-2010, Sections 4–7, Ventilation for Acceptable Indoor Air Quality (with errata) or the local equivalent, whichever is more stringent.

Option 2: CEN Standards EN 15251-2007 and EN 13779-2007
Projects outside the United States may instead meet the minimum outdoor air requirements of CEN Standards EN 15251-2007 and EN 13779-2007.

Naturally ventilated spaces

For naturally ventilated spaces (and for mixed-mode systems when the mechanical ventilation is inactivated), determine the minimum outdoor air opening and space configuration requirements using the natural ventilation procedure from ASHRAE Standard 62.1-2010, Section 4, or a local equivalent, whichever is more stringent.

Also confirm that natural ventilation is a good strategy for the project by following the flow diagram in the **Chartered Institution of Building Services Engineers (CIBSE)** Applications Manual AM10, March 2005, Natural Ventilation in Nondomestic Buildings, Figure 2.8.

For all spaces

ASHRAE Standard 62.1-2010's <u>indoor air quality</u> procedure cannot be used to comply with this prerequisite.

Monitoring

Mechanically ventilated spaces:

Monitor outdoor air intake flow as follows:

For variable air volume systems, monitor the minimum outdoor air intake flow with an outdoor airflow measurement device. This device should measure the minimum outdoor air intake flow with an accuracy of +/-10% of the designed minimum outdoor airflow rate. An alarm should be activated when the outdoor airflow value varies by 15% or more from the outdoor airflow setpoint.

For constant-volume systems, balance outdoor airflow to the minimum outdoor airflow design rate stipulated by ASHRAE Standard 62.1-2010 (with errata) or higher. Install either a current transducer on the supply fan, an airflow switch, or a similar monitoring device.

Naturally ventilated spaces

Comply with at least one of the following strategies:

- Provide a direct exhaust airflow measurement device. This device must measure the exhaust airflow with an accuracy of +/-10%. An alarm should be activated when airflow values vary by 15% or more.

- Provide automatic indication devices on all natural ventilation openings intended to meet the minimum opening requirements. An alarm should be activated when any one of the openings is closed during occupied hours.

- Monitor carbon dioxide concentrations within each thermal zone. CO_2 monitors must be between 3 and 6 feet (900 and 1,800 millimeters) above the floor and should be within each thermal zone. CO_2 monitors should have an audible or visual indicator to alert the building automation system if CO_2 concentration exceeds the maximum rate by more than 10%. Calculate appropriate CO_2 setpoints by using the methods in ASHRAE 62.1-2010, Appendix C.

KEY THINGS TO REMEMBER

- ASHRAE's standard numbers and their scopes are favorite test questions. **ASHRAE Standard 62.1-2010** is used for indoor air quality.

ENVIRONMENTAL TOBACCO SMOKE CONTROL—PREREQUISITE

PREREQUISITE SUMMARY

This prerequisite requires strict requirements to prevent smoking both outside and inside the building, thereby increasing the air quality and at the same time saving nonsmokers from the effects of secondhand smoke.

For schools, the prerequisite restricts smoke on the entire site without any exceptions.

PREREQUISITE INTENT

Preventing exposure of building users, indoor areas, and air distribution systems to environmental tobacco smoke.

PREREQUISITE REQUIREMENTS

Prohibit smoking inside the building. Also prohibit smoking outside the building except in designated smoking areas located at least **25 feet (7.5 meters)** from all entries, outdoor air intakes, and operable windows. In addition, prohibit smoking outside the property line in spaces that are used for business purposes.

If the requirement to prohibit smoking within 25 feet (7.5 meters) cannot be implemented because of code, documentation should be provided showing those regulations.

Signage must be posted within 10 feet (3 meters) of all building entrances to indicate the no-smoking policy.

For residential projects only: Meet one of the following options.

Option 1: No Smoking
    Meet the requirements above.

OR

Option 2: Compartmentalization of Smoking Areas
    In addition to the outside smoking requirements above, prohibit smoking inside all common areas of the building. The prohibition must be communicated in building rental or lease agreements as well.

Since there may be smoking inside each residential unit, each unit must be compartmentalized to prevent excessive leakage between units:

- All exterior doors and operable windows in the residential units should be weather-stripped to minimize leakage from outdoors.
- All doors leading from residential units into common hallways should be weather-stripped.
- By sealing penetrations in the walls, ceilings, and floors and by sealing vertical chases, minimize uncontrolled pathways for the transfer of smoke and other indoor air pollutants between residential units.
- Demonstrate a maximum leakage of 0.23 cubic feet per minute per square foot at 50 Pa of enclosure (e.g., surfaces enclosing the apartment, exterior, and party walls, floors, ceilings, etc.)
- For schools, no smoking is allowed on the <u>entire site</u>.

KEY THINGS TO REMEMBER

- For schools, LEED restricts smoking on the entire site without any exceptions.
- LEED requires to prohibit smoking outside the buildings except in designated smoking areas located at least **25 feet (7.5 meters)** from all entries, outdoor air intakes, and operable windows.
- In residential projects, each residential unit must be compartmentalized to prevent excessive leakage between units.

ENHANCED INDOOR AIR QUALITY STRATEGIES—CREDIT

- 1–2 Points

CREDIT SUMMARY

This is the credit of the "Minimum Indoor Air Quality Performance" prerequisite. It goes beyond the prerequisite and aims to enhance indoor air quality by requiring the installation of entryway systems to prevent contaminants brought inside the building, by setting increased ventilation rates, by encouraging the use of enhanced filtration media, and by monitoring building air quality.

The credit requires certain MERV ratings to be achieved in the air filters used in the project even though using air filters with a higher MERV will result in greater energy usage. As mentioned, the minimum efficiency reporting value rates the air filters according to their performance on removing particles from the air, and the higher the MERV, the more particles will be removed.

CREDIT INTENT

Promoting building occupants' well-being, comfort, and productivity by enhancing indoor air quality.

CREDIT REQUIREMENTS

Option 1: Enhanced IAQ Strategies—1 Point

In mechanically ventilated spaces, apply all three strategies below:
A. Entryway systems
B. Interior cross-contamination prevention
C. Filtration

In naturally ventilated spaces, apply both of the strategies below:
A. Entryway systems
D. Natural ventilation design calculations

In mixed-mode systems, apply all five following strategies:
A. Entryway systems

B. Interior cross-contamination prevention

C. Filtration

D. Natural ventilation design calculations

E. Mixed-mode design calculations

Let's take a closer look at the requirements of the mentioned strategies:

A. <u>Entryway systems</u>: Install permanent entryway systems to capture dirt and particulates at the regularly used exterior entrances. Some examples of entryway systems may be **grilles, grates, slotted systems,** and **rollout mats.** In addition, entryway systems should be maintained on a weekly basis.

B. <u>Interior cross-contamination prevention</u>: Exhaust spaces that may contain hazardous materials or chemicals according to the exhaust rates determined in the "Minimum Indoor Air Quality Performance" prerequisite should be prevented from contaminating other spaces. Spaces may include printing rooms, garages, laundry areas, etc.

C. <u>Filtration</u>: Each supply air (outdoor air) filter in the building should have a filter with a **MERV rating of 13 or higher according to ASHRAE 52.2-2007.** And all of the filters should be replaced after construction and before occupancy.

D. <u>Natural ventilation design calculations</u>: Occupied spaces system design should employ the appropriate strategies in **Chartered Institution of Building Services Engineers (CIBSE) Applications Manual AM10, March 2005, Natural Ventilation in Nondomestic Buildings, Section 2.4.**

E. <u>Mixed-mode design calculations</u>: Occupied spaces system design should comply with **CIBSE Applications Manual 13-2000, mixed mode ventilation.**

AND/OR

Option 2: Additional enhanced IAQ Strategies—1 Point

Mechanically ventilated spaces (select one strategy below):

A. Exterior contamination prevention

B. Increased ventilation

C. Carbon dioxide monitoring

D. Additional source control and monitoring

Naturally ventilated spaces (select one strategy below):

A. Exterior contamination prevention

D. Additional source control and monitoring

E. Natural ventilation room-by-room calculations

Mixed-mode systems (select one strategy below):

A. Exterior contamination prevention

B. Increased ventilation

D. Additional source control and monitoring

E. Natural ventilation room-by-room calculations

Let's take a closer look at the requirements of the mentioned strategies:

A. <u>Exterior contamination prevention</u>: Through computational fluid dynamics modeling, minimize the entry of pollutants into the building.

B. <u>Increased ventilation</u>: Increase all the ventilation rates by 30% above the minimum rates determined in the "Minimum Indoor Air Quality Performance" prerequisite.

C. <u>Carbon dioxide monitoring</u>: In all the densely occupied spaces, monitor carbon dioxide levels.

D. <u>Additional source control and monitoring</u>: Install monitoring systems to detect specific contaminants.

E. <u>Natural ventilation room-by-room calculations</u>: Implement CIBSE AM10, Section 4, design calculations.

KEY THINGS TO REMEMBER

- Grilles, grates, slotted systems, and rollout mats can be used in exterior building entrances to capture dirt under the entryway systems strategy.
- For enhanced indoor air quality, projects should use supply (outdoor) filters with a MERV rating of 13 or higher, according to ASHRAE 52.2-2007.
- Chartered Institution of Building Services Engineers (CIBSE).

LOW EMITTING MATERIALS—CREDIT

- 1–3 Points

CREDIT SUMMARY

The levels of the volatile organic compounds (VOCs) contained in the building materials are important to address since during the installation and operations phases, the material will release the VOCs indoors; consequently, this will present a serious health hazard for both the construction workers and the building occupants.

Think about epoxy-based paints. During the painting process, their smell is not pleasant at all. They release very strong odors, which can even create a burning feeling in the throat and lungs. This is caused by a high VOC level. Materials with a high level of VOCs can cause asthma, chronic obstructive pulmonary disease, and cancer while also causing harm to the environment.

The credit requires certain VOC levels to be met according to both material type and their location in the building; the materials are categorized as either interior or exterior materials. **In LEED, "building interior" is defined as everything inside the waterproofing membrane. And "building exterior" is everything outside the waterproofing membrane, including the waterproofing membrane.**

If the project meets the VOC requirements for some of the building materials, the project team can use the **budget calculation method** to earn the credit and show that the overall VOC level in the building is less than the required level by calculating the weighted averages of each material's VOC level. In LEED, the term <u>low-emitting</u> always refers to the VOC content.

Inherently nonemitting sources, which are products without any VOC emissions, do not need to be tested and will be exempt from this credit. Examples of inherently nonemitting sources are ceramic, stone, powder-coated metals, concrete, glass, anodized metal, clay brick, and untreated solid wood flooring.

CREDIT INTENT

Reducing the concentrations of chemical contaminants that may negatively affect the air quality, human health, productivity, and the environment.

CREDIT REQUIREMENTS

This credit addresses the VOC emissions into the indoor air by setting VOC limit thresholds to the materials' VOC content. The credit has different requirements for each material category.

Option 1: Product Category Calculations—1–3 Points
There are 7 material categories with different VOC thresholds.

Material category
Interior paints and coating applied on-site
Interior adhesives and sealants applied on-site
Flooring
Composite wood
Ceilings, walls, thermal, and acoustic insulation
Furniture
For healthcare and school only: Exterior-applied products

Table 22

If the materials used on-site achieve the threshold values of these material categories, then this option could be pursued. If there are some materials that can't meet the VOC requirements, project teams should pursue option 2.

OR

Option 2: Budget Calculation Method—1–3 Points
The budget method organizes the building interior into five assemblies:

- Flooring
- Ceilings
- Walls
- Thermal and acoustic insulation
- Furniture

According to each assembly type, projects should determine the total percentage of compliant materials. The average percentage of these 5 assemblies will determine the points earned. Table 23 shows how many points projects can receive for their percentage compliances.

If 90% of an assembly meets the criteria, the system will count it as 100% compliant. If less than 50% of an assembly meets the criteria, the assembly will be counted as 0% compliant.

Points for percentage compliance under option 2	
Percentage of total	Points
Between 50% and 69%	1
Between 70% and 89%	2
Equal to or more than 90%	3

Table 23

KEY THINGS TO REMEMBER

- Definition of building interior and building exterior.
- Definition of inherently nonemitting sources.
- Purpose of budget calculation method.

CONSTRUCTION INDOOR AIR QUALITY MANAGEMENT PLAN—CREDIT

- 1 Point

CREDIT SUMMARY

This credit requires the implementation of an indoor air quality management plan to reduce exposure of the building occupants to construction dust, toxic substances, or other contaminants. During construction, dust results in indoor contamination, which can stay in the building long after the construction is complete.

Think about the HVAC ducts stored inside the construction area without any dust protection; after their installation, they are supposed to provide fresh air to the building occupants. Nevertheless, it is clear that the dusty fresh air they will supply will not be very healthy for the building occupants.

The credit sets requirements to ensure a good standard of indoor air quality for building occupants immediately following the construction period. These requirements include the implementation of SMACNA IAQ guidelines, the replacement of the HVAC filtration media before occupancy (if HVAC is used during construction), and the prohibition of smoking inside and within 25 feet (7.5 meters) of the building during the construction phase. In addition, projects need to implement an **indoor air quality management plan** during the construction and preoccupancy phases in order to prevent molds and moisture damage and to increase the HVAC equipment performance and durability.

CREDIT INTENT

Minimizing indoor air quality problems caused by construction and renovation to promote the well-being of construction workers and building occupants.

CREDIT REQUIREMENTS

Develop and implement an **indoor air quality management plan** for the construction and preoccupancy phases of the building. The plan must address all of the following:
- During construction, meet or exceed all applicable control measures of the **Sheet Metal and Air Conditioning National Contractors Association (SMACNA) IAQ Guidelines for Occupied Buildings under Construction, 2nd edition, 2007, ANSI/SMACNA 008-2008, Chapter 3.**
- Protect absorptive materials that are installed or stored on-site from moisture damage.

❧ Do not operate permanently installed air-handling equipment during construction unless with filtration media with a minimum efficiency reporting value of 8—as determined by **ASHRAE 52.2-2007**, with errata (or as defined by CEN Standard EN779-2002 with a filtration media class of F5 or higher). The filtration media are installed at each return air grille and return or transfer duct inlet opening, and it is ensured that there is no bypass around the filtration media. Just before the occupancy, all the air filtration media should be replaced with the designed filtration media.

❧ Prohibit the use of tobacco products inside the building and within 25 feet (8 meters) of the building entrance during construction.

KEY THINGS TO REMEMBER

■ ASHRAE standards may be the favorite among standards, but it's also important to know that SMACNA guidelines address indoor air quality during construction.

■ ASHRAE 52.2-2007 is a standard related to air filters.

■ To protect indoor air quality, the filters of the HVAC equipment must be changed in case the HVAC system is used during construction.

INDOOR AIR QUALITY ASSESSMENT—CREDIT

- 1–2 Points

CREDIT SUMMARY

This credit is very similar to the previous "Construction Indoor Air Quality Management Plan" credit, but its requirements are different. The goal is again to provide good indoor air quality to the building occupants after the construction period. However, with this credit, projects are required to either remove the air pollution resulting from the construction activities by conducting a **flush-out**, or they are required to conduct an air testing inside the building to determine the air contamination levels, and take the necessary actions to clean the contamination, if exists. A flush-out refers to the process of supplying a sufficient amount of fresh air to the building before or during occupancy to take away the contaminated air and establish the desired level of indoor air quality.

CREDIT INTENT

To provide better indoor air quality in the building after the construction phase and during the occupancy phase.

CREDIT REQUIREMENTS

Choose one of the following options and implement it right after the construction ends and the building is completely cleaned. All interior finishes (doors, carpets, ceiling, etc.) must be installed, and major VOC punchlist items should be finished at the time of performing one of the following options.

Option 1: Flush-Out—1 Point

> Path 1: Before Occupancy
> Install new filtration media after the construction and perform a flush-out. For a flush-out, **14,000 cubic feet** of outdoor air per square foot of gross floor area should be supplied to the building while maintaining an internal temperature between 60°F and 80°F (15°C–27°C) and relative humidity not higher than 60%.

OR

Path 2: During Occupancy

If occupancy is desired before the completion of the flush-out, this path can be chosen. Before the occupancy, **3,500 cubic feet** of outdoor air per square foot of gross floor area must be provided to the building while maintaining an internal temperature between 60°F and 80°F (15°C–27°C) and relative humidity not higher than 60%.

After the space is occupied, the building must be ventilated at a minimum rate of 0.30 cubic foot per minute (cfm) per square foot of outdoor air. If the design rate determined in the "Minimum Indoor Air Quality Performance" prerequisite is greater than 0.3 cfm, that value must be used. During each day of the flush-out, the ventilation should start 3 hours before the occupancy and continue during the occupancy. This should continue until a total of **14,000 cubic feet** per square foot of outdoor air is delivered to the building.

OR

Option 2: Air testing—2 Points

Right after construction and before the occupancy, conduct a baseline indoor air quality test. For the test methodology, the current versions of ASTM standard methods, EPA compendium methods, or ISO methods can be used. The test should look at the values of formaldehyde, particulates, ozone, TVOCs (total volatile organic compounds), carbon monoxide, and some target chemical levels, and the test should determine if the air quality is suitable for occupancy. During the test, the HVAC system should be operated at the minimum outdoor airflow rate as when the building was occupied, and the test should be conducted during an hour when the building would normally be occupied even though the test would occur before occupancy. If the test fails, project teams should improve the air quality and conduct another test.

KEY THINGS TO REMEMBER

- Definition of flush-out
- The procedure and requirements of flush-out

THERMAL COMFORT—CREDIT

- 1 Point

CREDIT SUMMARY

Thermal comfort is one of the top priority measures to increase occupant comfort, and it is defined by a combination of six factors: air temperature, humidity, surface temperature, air movement, metabolic rate, and clothing. The thermal comfort ranges will be different, almost comparable to a basketball play where lots of people are moving at the same time, as compared to an office room with lots of people working inside without much physical activity.

Building users who are given thermal controls for their spaces will exhibit additional satisfaction and productivity. Giving occupants local temperature controls for +/- 5^0 F will be enough to increase their productivity by 2.7% to 7%.[1]

The credit requires projects to increase the comfort of the building occupants through the implementation of good thermal comfort design and the provision of thermal comfort controls to at least 50% of the individual occupant spaces.

CREDIT INTENT

Promote building occupants' productivity, well-being, and comfort by providing quality thermal comfort.

CREDIT REQUIREMENTS

Meet the requirements for both thermal comfort design and thermal comfort control:

Thermal comfort design:

Option 1: ASHRAE Standard 55-2010
Design HVAC systems and the building envelope to meet the requirements of **ASHRAE Standard 55-2010, Thermal Comfort Conditions for Human Occupancy, with errata or a local equivalent.**

For natatoriums only, demonstrate compliance with ASHRAE HVAC Applications Handbook, 2011 edition, Chapter 5, Places of Assembly, Typical Natatorium Design Conditions, with errata.

OR

Option 2: ISO and CEN Standards

Design HVAC systems and the building envelope to meet the requirements of the applicable standard:

- ISO 7730:2005, Ergonomics of the Thermal Environment, analytical determination and interpretation of thermal comfort, using calculation of the PMV and PPD indices and local thermal comfort criteria
- CEN Standard EN 15251:2007, Indoor Environmental Input Parameters for Design and Assessment of Energy Performance of Buildings, addressing indoor air quality, thermal environment, lighting, and acoustics, Section A2

Thermal comfort control:

Individual thermal comfort controls should be provided for at least 50% of the individual occupant spaces. In addition, the project teams should provide group thermal comfort controls for all shared multioccupant spaces and for any individual occupant spaces without individual controls.

All the thermal comfort controls provided should allow occupants to adjust at least one of the following in their local environment: <u>air temperature</u>, <u>radiant temperature</u>, <u>air speed, and humidity</u>.

KEY THINGS TO REMEMBER

- Individual thermal comfort controls should be provided for at least 50% of the individual occupant spaces.
- ASHRAE Standard 55-2010 is a standard on Thermal Comfort Conditions for Human Occupancy.
- Thermal comfort is one of the top priority measures to increase occupant comfort, which is defined by a combination of six factors: air temperature, humidity, surface temperature, air movement, metabolic rate, and clothing.

INTERIOR LIGHTING—CREDIT

- 1–2 Points

CREDIT SUMMARY

As is the case with thermal comfort, interior lighting is another factor that affects the productivity and comfort of building occupants. In summary, carefully illuminated spaces with lighting controls provided for individuals and groups result in increased comfort levels and productivity rates.

This credit aims to provide good interior lighting by requiring the projects to provide lighting controls for at least 90% of the individual occupant spaces and/or meet the following lighting quality standards under option 2.

To measure the amount of illumination that falls onto a surface, the term **foot-candle** is used, which is equal to one lumen per square foot.

CREDIT INTENT

Promoting building occupants' productivity, well-being, and comfort through high-quality lighting.

CREDIT REQUIREMENTS

Pursue one or both of the following two options.

Option 1: Lighting control—1 point
For at least **90%** of the <u>individual occupant spaces</u>, provide individual lighting controls that enable occupants to adjust the lighting to suit their preferences. The individual lighting controls should contain at **least three lighting levels (on, off, midlevel)**. Midlevel should be between 30% and 70% of the maximum illumination level (daylight contributions are not included).

For all <u>shared multioccupant spaces</u>, all of the following requirements should be met:

- Provide multizone control systems that enable occupants to adjust the lighting to meet group needs with at least three lighting levels or scenes (on, off, midlevel)
- Lighting for any presentation or projection wall must be separately controlled by the occupants

➤ Switches or manual controls must be in the same space with the controlled luminaires. The person operating the controls should be able to have direct line of sight to the controlled luminaires.

AND/OR

Option 2: Lighting quality—1 point

Choose four of the eight following strategies:

1. Use light fixtures with a luminance of less than 2,500 cd/m2 between 45 and 90 degrees from nadir for all regularly occupied spaces.
2. Use light sources with a CRI of 80 or higher for the entire project.
3. For 75% of the total connected lighting load, the light sources should have a rated life (or L70 for LED sources) of at least 24,000 hours (at 3 hours per start, if applicable).
4. For all regularly occupied spaces, use direct-only overhead lighting for 25% or less of the total connected lighting load.
5. For 90% of the regularly occupied floor area, projects should meet the following thresholds for area-weighted average surface reflectance: 85% for ceilings, 60% for walls, and 25% for floors.
6. Select furniture finishes to meet the following thresholds for area-weighted average surface reflectance: 45% for work surfaces and 50% for movable partitions.
7. For 75% of the regularly occupied floor area, meet the ratio of average wall surface illuminance to average work plane illuminance in order not to exceed 1:10. Strategies 5 and 6 should be also met or there should be a demonstration of area-weighted surface reflectance of 60% for walls.
8. For 75% of the regularly occupied floor area, meet a ratio of average ceiling illuminance to work surface illuminance that does not exceed 1:10. Strategies 5 and 6 should also be met, or there should be a demonstration of area-weighted surface reflectance of 85% for ceilings.

KEY THINGS TO REMEMBER

■ To increase occupant comfort, individual lighting controls should be provided for **90%** of the individual occupant spaces and should contain at least three lighting levels (on, off, mid-level).

■ Foot-candle is a measurement of the amount of illumination that falls on to a surface; a footcandle is equal to one lumen per square foot.

DAYLIGHT—CREDIT

- 1–3 Points

CREDIT SUMMARY

Studies show that increased access to daylight presents lots of benefits to human health and psychology. Exposure to daylight improves student performances[2] and patient healing times, increases productivity in offices,[3] and helps to fight depression. By introducing daylight into interior spaces, projects will also reduce lighting costs. However, the project teams should also consider the heat gains and losses that will result from daylighting.

This credit sets requirements for daylight qualities and levels, and points are awarded according to the daylight modeling process used and the percentage of the floor area with daylight access.

To maximize daylight in interior spaces, there can be use of transparent partitions or interior glazing such as interior windows placed in walls or doors. Low-height partitions in open offices can also increase the amount of daylight.

One problem with daylighting is the glare that the sun creates. The use of <u>operable</u> glare-control devices, such as operable window blinds or curtains, is required in this credit. <u>Fixed</u> glare-control devices—such as fixed exterior overhangs, fixed fins, fixed louvres, dark-colored glazing, frit glazing treatment, or additional glazing treatments—will not satisfy this credit. Acceptable glare control devices include interior window blinds, interior shades, curtains, moveable exterior louvres, moveable screens, and moveable awnings.

This credit also mentions **spatial daylight autonomy (sDA)**, which is a metric used to describe the annual sufficiency of ambient daylight in building interiors.

CREDIT INTENT

Connecting building occupants with the outdoors, reinforcing circadian rhythms, and reducing power consumption of electrical lighting by using daylight.

CREDIT REQUIREMENTS

Provide automatic (with manual override) or manual glare-control devices for all regularly occupied spaces. And then select one of the following three options:

Option 1: Simulation: Spatial Daylight Autonomy—2–3 points

Implement a computer simulation and demonstrate that spatial daylight autonomy (sDA) 300/50% (sDA300/50%) of at least 55%, or 75%. Use the regularly occupied floor area in the simulation. Points will be awarded according to table 24:

sDA for regularly occupied floor area	Points
55%	2
75%	3

Table 24

AND

By performing computer simulations, demonstrate that annual sunlight exposure 1000,250 (ASE1000,250) of no more than 10% is achieved. Use the regularly occupied floor area that is daylit per the sDA300/50% simulations. An hourly time-step analysis based on typical meteorological annual data should be used from the nearest available weather station. Include any permanent interior obstructions to sunlight. Movable furniture and partitions can be excluded.

OR

Option 2: Simulation: Illuminance calculations—1–2 Points

With the use of computer modeling, demonstrate that the illuminance levels will be between 300 lux and 3,000 lux from 9:00 a.m. to 3:00 p.m. (both on clear-sky days at the equinoxes) for the floor area percentages indicated in table 25. Use regularly occupied floor area.

% of regularly occupied floor area	Points
75%	1
90%	2

Table 25

Calculate illuminance intensity for the sun (direct component) and sky (diffuse component) for clear-sky conditions as follows:

- Use typical meteorological annual data of the nearest available weather station.
- Select one day within 15 days of September 21 and the other day within 15 days of March 21 to represent the clearest sky condition
- The average of the hourly value should be used for the two selected days

Blinds or shades, moveable furniture, and partitions may be excluded from the model. Any permanent interior obstructions to sunlight should be included.

OR

Option 3: Measurement—2–3 Points
Achieve illuminance levels between 300 lux and 3,000 lux for the percentage of floor area indicated by table 26:

% of regularly occupied floor area	Points
75%	1
90%	2

Table 26

With furniture, fixtures, and equipments all in place, measure illuminance levels as follows:

- ☛ Measure at appropriate work plane height between 9:00 a.m. and 3:00 p.m.
- ☛ Take one measurement in any regularly occupied month and the second one as specified in table 27.
- ☛ Spaces larger than 150 square feet (14 square meters) should have measurements taken on a maximum 10-foot (3 meter) square grid.
- ☛ For spaces of 150 square feet (14 square meters) or smaller, take measurements on a maximum 3-foot (900 millimeters) square grid.

If the first measurement was in,	then the second measurement should be in,
January	May—September
February	June—October
March	June-July, November—December
April	August—December
May	September—January
June	October—February
July	November—March
August	December—April
September	December—January, May—June
October	February—June
November	March—July
December	April—August

Table 27

KEY THINGS TO REMEMBER

- Definition of spatial daylight autonomy (sDA).
- Operable glare control devices such as operable window blinds/curtains are required in this credit. In LEED, fixed glare control devices, like fixed exterior overhangs, fixed fins, fixed louvres, dark-colored glazing, frit glazing treatment, or additional glazing treatments do not qualify as glare control devices. The acceptable ones are interior window blinds, interior shades, curtains, movable exterior louvres, movable screens, and movable awnings.
- To maximize daylight in interior spaces, transparent partitions or interior glazing can be used. One example would be interior windows placed in walls or doors. Using low-height partitions in open offices will also increase the amount of daylight.
- Daylighting is addressed under the Indoor Environmental Quality credit category, not Energy and Atmosphere.

QUALITY VIEWS—CREDIT

- 1 Point

CREDIT SUMMARY

Quality views are another factor in addressing occupant comfort and productivity. In offices, occupants who have a visual connection with outdoor environments demonstrate increased productivity. In hospitals, patients who have a decent view and access to nature can have reduced healing periods.[4] Projects that consider building orientation, interior layout, and building envelope to create quality views will therefore achieve a much greater level of occupant satisfaction.

This credit awards projects that provide a direct line of sight to the outdoors via vision glazing. Vision glazing should allow a clear image of the outdoors and should also be free of frits, patterns, fibers, or tints that disturb the color of the view. In open offices, partial-height/low-height partitions can be used to achieve quality views, or, instead, the partitions can be eliminated. This strategy would also support the previous "Daylighting" credit.

CREDIT INTENT

Providing building occupants connection with the natural outdoor environment by providing quality views.

CREDIT REQUIREMENTS

Achieve a direct line of sight to the outdoors via vision glazing for 75% of all the regularly occupied floor area. View glazing should provide a clear image of the outside and should not be obstructed by frits, fibers, patterned glazing, or added tints that distort color balance.

Additionally, 75% of all regularly occupied floor area must meet at least two of the following four view criteria:
- Multiple lines of sight to vision glazing in different directions at least 90 degrees apart
- Views that include at least two of the following: a) flora, fauna, or sky; b) movement; and c) objects at least 25 feet from the exterior of the glazing
- Unobstructed views located within a distance of three times the head height of the vision glazing
- Views with a view factor of 3 or greater, which is defined according to "Windows and Offices; A Study of Office Worker Performance and the Indoor Environment"

In the calculations, all the permanent interior obstructions should be included; <u>movable furniture</u> and <u>partitions</u> can be excluded. Views into the interior atria can be used to meet up to 30% of the required quality view area.

KEY THINGS TO REMEMBER

- View glazing should allow a clear image of the exterior and should not be obstructed by <u>frits</u>, <u>fibers</u>, <u>patterned glazing</u>, or <u>added tints that distort color balance</u>.
- In open offices, partial-height/low-height partitions can be used to allow for quality views, or the partitions can be eliminated.

ACOUSTIC PERFORMANCE—CREDIT

- 1 Point

CREDIT SUMMARY

Acoustic performance is essential in all building types for human comfort, privacy, productivity, and increased human health. Think about hearing everything from your neighbor next door because of the low acoustic quality of the interior partitions, which can easily lead to sleep disturbance and stress. In classrooms, students' concentration levels can easily be disturbed by outside noises. In hospitals with poor acoustic qualities, patients can face even more consequences.

This credit awards points for establishing a high acoustic quality via reducing HVAC background noise by using sound reinforcement and **masking systems**, by establishing sound isolation, and by requiring certain amounts of **reverberation time**.

Masking systems, or sound masking systems, are equipments used to reduce the background noise in spaces. Nowadays, masking systems are very popular for use in open offices in order to establish good acoustical quality.

Reverberation time is the time span between when a sound is produced and when it dies away. Actually, sounds do not merely die away; in fact, they are absorbed by the materials, furniture, and isolation products while they reach zero amplitude.

CREDIT INTENT

Providing classrooms, workspaces, and other occupied spaces effective acoustic design that promotes the well-being, communications, and productivity of the building occupants.

CREDIT REQUIREMENTS

For all occupied spaces, meet the following requirements for HVAC background noise, sound isolation, reverberation time, and sound reinforcement/masking.

HVAC Background Noise:
Achieve maximum background noise levels from HVAC systems per **2011 ASHRAE Handbook**, HVAC Applications, Chapter 48, Table 1; AHRI Standard 885-2008, Table 15; or a local equivalent. Measure sound levels.

For measurements, the sound level meter should conform to ANSI S1.4 for type 1 (precision) or type 2 (general purpose) sound measurement instrumentation or a local equivalent.

Comply with design criteria for HVAC noise levels resulting from the sound transmission paths listed in ASHRAE 2011 Applications Handbook, Table 6 or a local equivalent.

Sound Isolation:
Projects should meet the composite sound transmission class (STCc) ratings as specified by USGBC.

Reverberation Time:
Projects should meet the reverberation time requirements in the Performance Measurement Protocols for Commercial Buildings.

Sound Reinforcement and Masking Systems:

Sound Reinforcement:
For all large conference rooms and auditoriums serving more than 50 people, the need for sound reinforcement options should be evaluated.

Masking Systems:
For projects that use masking systems, the design levels should not exceed 48 dBA.

KEY THINGS TO REMEMBER

- For acoustic performance, LEED requires implementing measures for HVAC background noise, sound transmission, reverberation time, sound reinforcement, and masking systems.
- The 2011 ASHRAE Handbook, HVAC Applications, is used to address HVAC background noise.
- Usage of masking systems.
- The definition of reverberation time.

CHAPTER 11

INNOVATION (IN)

The innovation credit category encourages exploration and implementation of new green building technologies to create additional environmental benefits, as well as exceeding the thresholds defined in the LEED credits.

Six total points are available in this credit category, with four different strategies:

- Innovative strategy
- Exemplary performance
- Pilot credits
- Including a LEED Accredited Professional on the project team

INNOVATIVE STRATEGY

LEED encourages projects to exceed green building principles with new and unique ways of implementations that have not been previously covered in the LEED rating systems. If projects can create their own innovations, they can then receive extra points under the "Innovation" credit.

An example might be to relocate or transplant trees on-site, rather than removing them. The project team could create a credit called "Tree Transplanting" and send it to GBCI as an innovation credit.

The innovation credit created should meet the following criteria:

- Demonstrate a quantitative improvement in environmental performance by showing the comparison of its baseline values
- Establish a comprehensive strategy that cannot be limited to the use of a single product and can be applied to the entire project
- The innovated credit should be significantly better than the standard sustainable design practices

EXEMPLARY PERFORMANCE

For eligible LEED credits, a performance beyond the LEED credit requirements will earn projects exemplary performance points, which are generally achieved by doubling the credit requirements and/or achieving the next incremental percentage threshold.

In the "Site Development—Protect or Restore Habitat" credit, projects can earn this credit by restoring 30% of the previously developed land by using native or adapted vegetation. If the project can restore 60% of the previously developed land, the project will be awarded an extra point for achieving a level of exemplary performance.

Another example would be the "Renewable Energy Production" credit. If the projects can produce 10% of their annual energy consumption by cost with on-site renewable energy sources, the credit will award 3 out of 3 points. If they can go beyond that and establish 15%, which is the exemplary performance threshold for that credit, an extra point will be awarded.

Don't forget that all the LEED credits are not eligible for exemplary performance; moreover, eligible credits have different requirements for exemplary performance.

INNOVATION—CREDIT

- 1–5 Points

CREDIT SUMMARY

To encourage project teams to go beyond LEED requirements and innovate new ways to achieve sustainable design, this credit awards extra points.

To achieve this credit, the projects can either create their own innovation credit and/or can choose pilot credits to pursue from the LEED pilot credit library and fulfill the requirements. (Because pilot credit availability changes over time, it is recommended to register for a pilot credit as soon as the project teams decide to go ahead with it.) In addition, or as an alternative, the project teams may choose to achieve exemplary performance from the eligible credits.

CREDIT INTENT

Encouraging projects to achieve exceptional or innovative performance.

CREDIT REQUIREMENTS

Project teams can use any combination of innovation, pilot, and exemplary performance strategies.

Option 1: Innovation—1 point
Achieve significant, measurable environmental performance using an innovative strategy that is not addressed in the LEED green building rating system.

Identify the following:
- The intent of the proposed innovation credit
- Proposed requirements for compliance
- Proposed submittals to demonstrate compliance
- Design approach or strategies used to meet the requirements

AND/OR

Option 2: Pilot—1 point
Achieve one pilot credit from USGBC's LEED Pilot Credit Library

AND/OR

Option 3: Additional strategies—1–3 points

Innovation—1–3 Points
- Defined in Option 1 above.

Pilot—1–3 points
- Meet the requirements of Option 2.

Exemplary performance—1–2 points
- Achieve exemplary performance in an existing LEED v4 credit that allows for exemplary performance. An exemplary performance point is typically earned for achieving double the credit requirements or the next incremental percentage threshold.

KEY THINGS TO REMEMBER

- The purpose of exemplary performance.
- The innovation credit contains 5 points, and the innovation credit category contains 6 points (with the "LEED Accredited Professional" credit).
- Requirements for earning an innovation point in LEED in credit option 1.
- The purpose of pilot credits in LEED (see "Pilot Credits").
- "Innovation," "Pilot," and "Exemplary Performance" points are all awarded under the innovation credit.
- The innovation credit created should meet the following criteria: demonstrate a quantitative improvement in environmental performance by showing the comparison of its baseline values, establish a comprehensive strategy that cannot be limited to the use of a single product and can be applied to the entire project, and establish an innovated credit that is significantly better than the standard sustainable design practices.

LEED ACCREDITED PROFESSIONAL—CREDIT

- 1 Point

CREDIT SUMMARY

The innovation credit category awards a point for having a LEED Accredited Professional (AP) with a specialty appropriate to the project as one of the principal participants of the project team, under this credit. Legacy LEED APs (LEED APs without specialty) do not qualify in this credit.

The selected LEED AP with specialty principal should have the active credential at the time of project's certification review.

CREDIT INTENT

To promote the team integration required for LEED projects and at the same time streamline the application and certification process.

CREDIT REQUIREMENTS

At least one principal participant of the project team must be a LEED Accredited Professional with a specialty appropriate for the project. A project employing a LEED AP O+M as a principal participant of the project team for a LEED BD+C project cannot earn the credit.

KEY THINGS TO REMEMBER

- Legacy LEED APs (LEED APs without a specialty) do not qualify in this credit.
- Projects can receive only 1 point under this credit even if they employ more than 1 LEED AP with a specialty appropriate for the project.

CHAPTER 12

REGIONAL PRIORITY (RP)

LEED projects span the entire globe. They exist in different climate zones and in different population densities, and they have different water and energy availabilities and different local problems to deal with. A credit may be much easier to achieve for a project in location A than a project in location B.

Since each location has different regional issues and different environmental problems, USGBC identifies 6 credits from the existing LEED credits in each rating system that contribute more to those regional issues for that particular location. And, if a project decides to earn some of those credits as a bonus, the project will also be awarded points from the "Regional Priority" credit, which is the only credit under the RP credit category. Projects can see the regional priority credits available for their location online at USGBC's website.

For example, a project located in Los Angeles, California, should first enter the exact project location in USGBC's "Regional Priority Lookup" page online. This web page will show the regional priority credits for that project's location. In this case, they are listed as the following:

- Optimize Energy Performance
- Surrounding Density and Diverse Use
- Access to Quality Transit

- Reduced Parking Footprint
- Rainwater Management
- Indoor Water Use Reduction

Let's say that the project has already earned the "Rainwater Management" and the "Access to Quality Transit" credits, which would also mean that the project would receive 2 bonus points from the "Regional Priority" credit in addition to the points received from the "Rainwater Management" and "Access to Quality Transit" credits.

For another location with low potable water availability, the "Indoor Water Use Reduction" and "Outdoor Water Use Reduction" credits could make up 2 of the 6 regional priority credits. Alternatively, if a specific location contained mostly sensitive lands, then the "Sensitive Land Protection" credit could be 1 of the 6 regional priority credits.

The "Regional Priority" credit contains 4 points, which means that if the project had achieved 4 out of the 6 regional priority credits, 4 points would thus be awarded. If the project had achieved 6 out of the 6 regional priority credits, 4 points would be awarded. If the project had achieved 2 out of the 6 regional priority credits, then 2 points would be awarded.

REGIONAL PRIORITY—CREDIT

- 1–4 Points

CREDIT INTENT

Establishing an incentive for the achievement of credits that addresses geographically specific environmental and public health priorities and social equity.

CREDIT REQUIREMENTS

There are 6 available Regional Priority credits for every location, and they are identified by the USGBC regional councils and chapters. The project should earn up to 4 of those 6 credits. The Regional Priority credits have been identified by the USGBC regional councils and chapters as having additional regional importance for the project's region. To see the database of regional priority credits and their geographic applicability, project teams should visit the USGBC's website.

One point will be awarded for each Regional Priority credit achieved, up to a maximum of four.

KEY THINGS TO REMEMBER

- The purpose of Regional Priority credits.
- Regional Priority credit contains 4 points.
- Regional Priority credits are identified by the USGBC regional councils and chapters.

CHAPTER 13

LEED® GREEN ASSOCIATE™ EXAM

EXAM REGISTRATION PROCESS

This chapter will give information about the LEED Green Associate exam; however it is also recommended that you visit the USGBC's website and download the latest LEED Green Associate Candidate Handbook.

ELIGIBILITY REQUIREMENTS

Test-takers must be 18 years of age or older and must also agree to the "Disciplinary and Exam Appeals Policy," which can be found on GBCI's website.

HOW TO REGISTER FOR THE EXAM?

1. If you have an existing USGBC site user account, log in to your credentials account to register for the exam, or create a new account if you don't have one. www.usgbc.org/credentials
2. Make sure that the name you enter exactly matches the name on the ID you will present at

the test center. If it does not match, please update your name on the website's user account "settings."

3. Review the address in the profile. (The certificate will be mailed to that address.)

4. Select the credential exam you wish to apply for, and follow the instructions to complete the application.

5. You will be redirected to prometric.com/gbci to schedule your exam date and location.

6. When the exam is scheduled, you will receive a confirmation number onscreen and an email through Prometric.

7. Print and keep your confirmation number. You will need this confirmation number to confirm, cancel, or reschedule your appointment through the Prometric website.

8. prometric.com/gbci.

9. Once you register and pay for your exam, you have one year to schedule your exam session. You may request one six-month extension of this one-year period.

WHERE TO TAKE THE EXAM?

The exam is administered by Prometric testing centers throughout the world.

EXAM FEES

The exam fee is $100 for students, $200 for USGBC members, and $250 for non members.

TESTING CENTER RULES

- All the test-takers should present a government-issued photo ID <u>that also contains a signature</u> at the Prometric testing center.
- Nothing can be brought to the exam. Small lockers may be available at the testing center to store your wallet, cell phone, keys, and other small items. However, laptops, briefcases, or large purses shouldn't be taken to the testing center.
- Scrap paper and pencils will be provided by the test site staff and will be collected at the conclusion of the exam. No other paper can be brought into the exam room.
- To leave the room during the exam, test-takers should get the test proctor's permission.
- Eating and drinking is not permitted in the exam room.

SPECIAL TESTING ACCOMMODATIONS

Accommodations can be requested in case you have a documented disability that would prevent you from taking the exam under normal testing conditions. Prometric complies with the provisions of the Americans with Disabilities Act (ADA).

Any special accommodation should be indicated during exam registration. There is no additional charge for special accommodations.

ABOUT THE EXAM

NO NEED TO BUY ADDITIONAL STUDY MATERIALS

By thoroughly studying this book, you can pass the exam with flying colors.

THE EXAM

The LEED Green Associate exam contains 100 randomly delivered multiple choice questions that must be completed in 2 hours.

The LEED AP exam contains two core parts. The first core part is the LEED Green Associate exam. The second part is the LEED AP with specialty exam, which also contains 100 randomly delivered multiple choice questions that should be completed in 2 hours. LEED Green Associates will only need to take the second core part of the LEED AP exam in order to earn a LEED AP credential.

The LEED AP exam can be taken in one sitting. In this case, the exam will take 4 hours. However, if the test-taker passes the first part of the exam, which is the LEED Green Associate exam, and subsequently fails the second part, the test-taker cannot earn the LEED Green Associate credential and must then retake the whole exam and pass both parts.

In the exam there will be both scored and unscored questions. Unscored questions are used to collect performance data for USGBC. Test-takers will not know if a question will be scored or unscored. As there are both scored and unscored questions in the exam, and the questions are also scaled, there's no way to know how many correct answers you need in order to pass the exam.

In order to pass all the LEED Professional exams, candidates must score 170 points out of 200 possible points. 125 is the minimum score in all the LEED Professional exams. If you are taking the LEED AP exam combined, you should score 170 or higher points in both core parts of the exam. At the end of the exam, you will be able to see your score on the computer screen.

If you have an appeal about the exam content, you can leave comments regarding any question in the exam in case you think there's a technical mistake; however, appeals must be made in the first 14 days after the test. If your appeal is approved, you will be able to take the test again, although your score for the first test will not change.

Make sure you read all the questions and the choices very carefully! If a question seems to have more than one answer, make sure you thoroughly understand the question and pay special attention to the wording. It doesn't matter how well you know the exam content; if you don't read the content very carefully, the exam can easily trick you into selecting the wrong answer.

EXAM CONTENT

The LEED Green Associate exam is intended to test knowledge of Task Domains and Knowledge Domains.

Task domains include the tasks necessary to perform LEED effectively, such as team coordination, certification process, LEED Online, and more. Knowledge Domains include the LEED process, LEED rating systems, credit categories, and more.

Below is the breakdown of the exam questions:

- LEED process
- Integrative strategies
- Location and transportation
- Sustainable sites
- Water efficiency
- Energy and atmosphere
- Materials and resources
- Indoor environmental quality
- Project surroundings and public outreach

Project surroundings and public outreach contains questions about values of sustainable design, regional design, environmental impacts and necessity of green buildings, triple bottom line, and more.

EXAM FORMAT

All the LEED credentialing exams are computer based. Exam questions and answer options will be displayed on screen.

Most of the exam questions are multiple choice questions that ask to choose the correct answer out of the displayed choices. However, some questions will have more than one answer, and those questions ask to choose 2 out of 4 choices, or 3 out of 5. And there will be no partial credit for choosing only one correct answer.

Test-takers can leave a question unanswered, flag questions for later review, and change the answer of any test question before the completion of the exam. If you have extra time at the end of your exam, it's highly recommended that you review all the questions.

On the exam answer every single question since leaving it blank will not result in any points. And if you're unsure about the answer, mark the question and come back to review it later.

During the exam, if you forget something, some questions or answer choices can make you remember the answer of another question.

EXAM TUTORIAL AND EXIT SURVEY

Before the exam, there will be a 10-minute tutorial to demonstrate the exam software. And at the end of the exam, there will be a 10-minute optional exit survey.

During the completion of the tutorial, you can write down any notes on the provided scratch paper that you think will be helpful during the exam.

WHAT TO EXPECT AT THE TEST CENTER

It is recommended that the test-takers arrive 30 minutes prior to the scheduled exam appointment. Test-takers who arrive later than their scheduled exam time will lose their seat.

Test center staff will escort the test-taker to a workstation, and the test-taker should remain seated during the exam unless authorized to leave by test center staff. In case there is a problem with the computer, or you need to take a break, raise your hand to notify the test center staff. However, the exam will not pause if you take a break.

All the test-takers should also obey Prometric's security rules while at the test center.

AFTER THE EXAM

EXAM RESULTS

After the exam, your exam score will be displayed on screen, and the test center staff will provide a printed report of your results.

PASSING THE EXAM

As soon as you have passed the exam, you can use the title "LEED® Green Associate™" and/or the logo. Please remember that the LEED GA abbreviation is disapproved by USGBC and cannot be used under any circumstances.

Your exam results will be processed within 3 days and, once processed, the certificate can be requested. The certificate will be available as a PDF softcopy that can be downloaded at any time for free, and as a hard copy that can be requested from USGBC's website for a fee.

If a LEED AP credential is earned after becoming a LEED Green Associate, your LEED Green Associate credential will be replaced by the LEED AP.

FAILING THE EXAM

The full exam fee will be charged for each scheduled exam session after failing an exam.

HOW TO MAINTAIN LEED CREDENTIALS

All the LEED Green Associates must earn 15 continuing education (CE) hours within 2 years of earning their credential while all the LEED APs will need to earn 30 continuing education (CE) hours within 2 years of earning their credential.

HOW TO KNOW YOU ARE READY

Before the exam, make sure you feel comfortable with:
- The terms in the "Glossary" section of this book
- The terms in the "Index" section of this book
- The refrigerant table (table 18)
- Appendix A showing the summary of the ASHRAE standards
- Appendix B showing other important standards and programs
- The summary of "strategies" at the end of the chapters through chapter 5—10
- Everything mentioned under "Key Things to Remember" sections at the end of every prerequisite/credit

Some people may also choose to take practice tests to reinforce knowledge; however, if you thoroughly studied this book and are also comfortable with the items listed above, you should not have any problems during the real exam.

Wish you all the best in your exam!

HOW TO ACCESS THE DIGITAL RESOURCES

Simply scan the QR code below with your phone, tablet, or any other capable device to access sample test questions online, and familiarize yourself with the actual exam format.

To truly evaluate and sustain our performance, each of us needs feedback. As we have discussed, without any feedback, no closed loop system can be created. That being said, please do submit any comments about this book, your test score, and/or any other feedback, online with this QR code.

APPENDIX A – SUMMARY OF ASHRAE STANDARDS

Name of the Standard / Program	Keywords	Related Prerequisites / Credits
ASHRAE Guideline 0-2005	Commissioning essentials	Prerequisite — Fundamental Comm. and Ver., Credit — Enhanced Commissioning
ASHRAE Guideline 1.1-2007	HVAC & R technical requirements for commissioning	Prerequisite — Fundamental Comm. and Ver., Credit — Enhanced Commissioning
ANSI/ASHRAE/IESNA Standard 90.1.-2010, Appendix G with errata	Used for the whole building energy simulation	Prerequisite — Minimum Energy Performance
ASHRAE Advanced Energy Design Guide	Advanced energy design guide	Prerequisite — Minimum Energy Perf., Credit — Optimize Energy Perf.
ASHRAE 90.1	Energy standard for buildings, also used to identify project's climate zone	Prerequisite — Minimum Energy Performance
ASHRAE 62.1-2010	Ventilation for acceptable indoor air quality	Prerequisite — Minimum Air Quality Performance
ASHRAE 52.2-2007	Air filter standards	Credit — Enhanced Indoor Air Quality Strategies
ASHRAE Standard 55–2010	Thermal comfort conditions for human occupancy	Credit — Thermal Comfort
2011 ASHRAE Handbook	Handbook about the HVAC applications, in the credit it relates to the HVAC background noise	Credit Acoustic Performance

APPENDIX B – IMPORTANT STANDARDS AND PROGRAMS

Name of the Standard / Program	Keywords	Related Prerequisites / Credits
ANSI Consensus National Standard Guide 2.0	Useful for implementing a successful integrative process	Credit — Integrative Process
US Department of Agriculture, US Code of Federal Regulations Title 7, Volume 6	Defines prime farmlands	Credit — Sensitive Land Protection
US Environmental Protection Agency (EPA), National Priority List	Defines National Priority sites	Credit — High Priority Site
US Housing and Urban Development	Defines Federal Empowerment Zone, Federal Enterprise Community, and Federal Renewal Community	Credit — High Priority Site
US Department of Treasury, Community Development Financial Institutions Fund	Provides funds for low-income communities	Credit — High Priority Site
Parking Consultants Council, Transportation Planning Handbook, 3rd edition	Provides base parking capacity ratios for buildings	Credit — Reduced Parking Footprint
American Council for an Energy-Efficient Economy (ACEEE)	Defines green vehicles (should score a minimum of 45 on ACEEE to qualify)	Credit — Green Vehicles
Illuminating Engineering Society of North America (IESNA)	Develops lighting specifications	Prerequisite — Minimum Energy Performance
2012 US Environmental Protection Agency (EPA), Construction General Permit (CGP)	Sets requirements for the erosion and sedimentation control (ESC) plan	Prerequisite — Construction Activity Pollution Prevention
Land Trust Alliance	Provides accreditation to land trust organizations	Credit — Site Development - Protect or Restore Habitat

Name of the Standard / Program	Keywords	Related Prerequisites / Credits
WaterSense	A program developed by EPA to identify high-performance, water-efficient fixtures and fittings	Prerequisite, Credit — Indoor Water Use Reduction
ENERGY STAR Portfolio Manager™	Interactive, online management tool that enables projects to track and assess energy and water consumption	
ENERGY STAR TargetFinder™	Allows projects to set target goals for building design's energy demands	
Home Energy Saver™	A do-it-yourself energy audit, which is developed by the US Department of Energy for existing buildings to analyze, reduce, and manage their energy use	
Montreal Protocol	Banned the production of chlorofluorocarbon (CFC) refrigerants and also phasing out hydrochlorofluorocarbon (HCFC) refrigerants	
Green-e	The leading certification program for the green power generation in the United States	Credit — Green Power and Carbon Offsets
Green-e Energy	Green power certification program	Credit — Green Power and Carbon Offsets
Green-e Climate	Carbon offset certification program	Credit — Green Power and Carbon Offsets
Advanced Buildings™ Core Performance Guide™	Energy design guide	Prerequisite — Minimum Energy Performance
National Institute of Building Sciences (NIBS) Guideline 3-2012, Exterior Enclosure Technical Requirements for the Cx Process	Used for the envelope commissioning	Credit — Enhanced Commissioning
US Department of Energy's Commercial Buildings Energy Consumption Survey (CBECS)	Database used to estimate a building's total energy cost	Credit — Renewable Energy Production
Energy Policy Act of 1992 (EPAct 1992)	Specifies baseline flow and flush rates	Prerequisite, Credit — Indoor Water Use Reduction

Name of the Standard / Program	Keywords	Related Prerequisites / Credits
Forest Stewardship Council (FSC)	A voluntary program which sets standards to wood product manufacturers to ensure responsible forest management in order to prevent deforestation and loss of habitat	Credit — BDPO Sourcing of Raw Materials
Extended Producer Responsibility (EPR)	Is a product stewardship policy approach that holds consumer goods companies responsible for managing their own products and packaging when consumers are finished with them	Credit — BDPO Sourcing of Raw Materials
Cradle to Cradle Certification (C2C)	Assesses the ingredients of a product according to environmental and human health hazards	Credit — BDPO Material Ingredients
GreenScreen	A method used to identify chemicals of high concern and safer alternatives	Credit — BDPO Material Ingredients
REACH Optimization	European Union's legislation that requires all chemicals sold to be evaluated based on their hazard profiles	Credit — BDPO Material Ingredients
Sheet Metal and Air Conditioning National Contractors Association (SMACNA) guidelines	Describes the necessary control measures to be taken during construction to protect indoor air quality	Credit — Construction Indoor Air Quality Management Plan
Chartered Institution of Building Services Engineers (CIBSE) Applications Manual AM10	About ventilation strategies	Credit — Enhanced Indoor Air Quality Strategies
US Environmental Protection Agency (EPA) WaterSense Water Budget Tool	Calculates landscape water requirements (LWR)	Prerequisite, Credit — Outdoor Water Use Reduction

40/60 rule: A method used to choose the appropriate rating system for the project if the project seems to fit under multiple rating systems.

Active daylighting: Is a system that tracks and collects the sunlight using mechanical devices, but they may not function well on cloudy days.

Adapted plants: Types of plants that do not occur naturally in a specific location; however, they can nonetheless adapt easily to the climate of the region.

Adjacent site: A site containing a previously developed site at its minimum 25% of the boundary bordering parcels.

Albedo: A type of reflectivity measurement from "0" to "1," which "0" represents black surfaces that absorb all the solar radiation, while "1" represents white surfaces that reflects all the solar radiation.

Alternative compliance paths (ACPs): Enable international projects to earn the appropriate prerequisites/credits by allowing them to meet international standards or their local standards instead of United States based standards.

Alternative fuel vehicles: Vehicles that consume nongasoline, low-polluting fuels like hydrogen, electricity, propane, compressed natural gas, liquid natural gas, methanol, or ethanol.

Alternative fuel: Low-polluting fuels like hydrogen, electricity, propane, compressed natural gas, liquid natural gas, methanol, or ethanol.

Alternative water source: Nonpotable water from on-site surfaces, or freshwater sources, such as graywater, on-site reclaimed water, collected rainwater, captured condensate, and rejected water from reverse osmosis systems. Water from public utilities is excluded.

Basis of design (BOD): Describes the information necessary to accomplish the owner's project requirements, which includes system requirements, design criteria, standards, and guidelines, developed by the architect/engineer.

Bio-based materials: Are products other than food that are biological products, renewable agricultural materials or forestry materials. Biobased materials are derived from biomass. Plants and animals can be an example of biobased materials, however, hide products, such as leather and other animal skin material are excluded in LEED calculations.

Biofuel: Fuels produced from organic material. Biofuel includes untreated wood waste, landfill gas, agricultural crops or waste, animal waste, and other types of organic waste.

Bioswale: A stormwater control feature which uses a combination of engineered basin, soils and vegetation.

Blackwater: Is the term to describe the used water that has come into contact with waste. Thus, the water collected from the urinals and toilets can be classified as blackwater.

Blowdown: Removal of the cooling tower's water in order to minimize deposit of scales.

Brownfield site: A previously developed site that was contaminated with waste or pollution. A site that is left from an abandoned building in which the contamination is not yet known can also be classified as a brownfield site.

BUG rating method: A luminaire classification system that classifies a luminaire according to backlight, uplight, and glare.

Building automation system (BAS): A computer-based monitoring system which can monitor, coordinate and control every individual building system.

Building exterior: Defined as everything from the waterproofing membrane, inclusive of the waterproofing membrane.

Building footprint: Describes the area that the building sits on.

Building interior: Defined as everything inside the waterproofing membrane.

Built environment: Refers to all the man-made surroundings that are needed for human activity, from roads, to buildings, to neighborhoods.

Carbon neutrality: To emit no more carbon emissions than can realistically be offset.

Carbon offset: Is a reduction of carbon dioxide (CO_2) made in order to compensate, or offset an equivalent carbon dioxide (CO_2) emission made elsewhere.

Chain of custody (CoC): Procedure of tracking a product from extraction/harvesting to its distribution. An example may be the FSC certification, which provides chain-of-custody certification for wood-based products.

Charrettes: Are intense workshops that are generally held at the beginning of the project and during the project milestones.

Chlorofluorocarbon (CFC)-based refrigerant: A refrigerant in fluid state containing hydrocarbons, which absorb heat at low temperatures and reject heat at higher temperatures.

Clean waste: Materials that are left over from construction and demolition that are nonhazardous.

Closed system: System that does not produce any waste product at the end by circulating the same median.

Commingled waste: Single-streamed waste for recycling.

Commissioning (Cx): Is a systematic investigation by skilled personnel that compares building performance with the project goals, design specifications, and, most importantly, the owner's project requirements (OPR).

Conventional irrigation: Common system used for irrigation, such as irrigation through sprinkler heads above the ground.

Corporate Sustainability Reports (CSR): Provides information about the manufacturer or raw-material supplier of a product that has been verified to employ sustainable principles during the creation of their products.

Cradle-to-cradle: Evaluates materials to have infinite life cycles through recycling to form a closed system.

Cradle-to-grave: Investigates materials from their extraction to their disposal.

Cradle-to-gate assessment: Evaluates a product's partial life cycle from its resource extraction/harvesting to becoming a manufactured product ready for sale at the factory gate.

Current facility requirements (CFR): Requirements to fulfill the owner's operational needs.

Demand response (DR): An intentional reduction in the electricity usage in response to a demand response (DR) event, or changes in the price of electricity.

Demand response event (curtailment event): The period that the utility company asks for a reduction in electricity usage from its program participants.

Development footprint: Named for the sum of all the areas that are affected by the project's activity in the project site.

District energy system (DES): A central energy conversion plant that provides thermal energy, shared by a group of buildings.

Diverse use: Publicly available businesses that provide daily need goods or services. According to USGBC, diverse uses do not include ATMs, vending machines and touch screens.

Diversion rate: Percentage of waste materials diverted from landfill.

Drip irrigation systems: Are the types of microirrigation systems that drip water to the roots of plants to minimize the use of irrigation water and fertilizers. They are the most water-efficient systems and have very short payback periods.

Dry ponds (detention ponds): Hold the excess rainwater for some time, thereby allowing the rainwater to slowly seep into the ground without contamination. Dry ponds are excavated areas that detain and slow down stormwater but are dry at other times.

EDUCATION @USGBC: Education portal of USGBC.

Embodied energy: The total energy consumed resulting from a product's manufacturing, transportation, installation, and use.

Emergent properties: Emergence of certain properties in the systems as a result of interaction of individual elements.

Emissivity (infrared or thermal emittance): Is a measure that shows how much heat or infrared radiation a material can shed back into the atmosphere.

Energy rater: Professionals with a HERS rater credential that conducts the performance testing in LEED for Homes projects.

Energy use intensity (EUI): A measurement unit that describes the building's energy usage relative to its size.

Environmental Product Declaration (EPD): Disclosure that looks at the entire life cycle of a product and assesses the cost of the product on the environment. Products that contain an EPD will give information about a product's impact on global warming, ozone depletion, water pollution, greenhouse gas emission, human toxicity, and more.

Erosion and sedimentation control (ESC) plan: A plan developed to prevent erosion, sedimentation, and stormwater pollution to the water bodies, wetlands, and the whole neighborhood.

Evapotranspiration: Is the term used for the return of water to the atmosphere through evaporation from plants.

Extended Producer Responsibility (EPR): Is a product stewardship policy approach that holds companies producing consumer goods responsible for managing their own products and packaging when consumers are finished with them.

Extensive vegetated roofs: Are the types of roofs that do not include a variety of plants and require little maintenance. Their soil layer is thinner compared with the intensive roofs since they are more designed for the smaller-sized vegetation.

Floor-to-area ratio (FAR): Is calculated by dividing the total square feet of a building by the total square feet of the lot of the building.

Flush-out: Is the process of supplying good amounts of fresh air to the building before or during occupancy to take away the contaminated air and establish the desired level of indoor air quality.

Foot-candle: A measure of the amount of illumination that falls on a surface, equal to one lumen per square foot.

Functional entry: Any building opening that is open and used by pedestrians during business hours.

Gallons per flush (gpf): A unit of measurement used to calculate the water usage of flush fixtures such as toilets and urinals.

Gallons per minute (gpm): A unit of measurement used to calculate the water usage of flow fixtures such as sink faucets, shower heads, and aerators.

Geothermal heat pumps: Also known as "geoexchange", or "ground source heat pumps," geothermal heat pumps are central heating and/or cooling systems that transfer heat to or from the ground. In winter, this system uses the earth as a heat source while in summer, the earth is used as a heat sink.

Graywater: Is the untreated household water that did not come into contact with toilet waste. Used water from bathtubs, showers, bathroom washbasins, and water from clothes washers and laundry tubs can be examples of graywater and may be used as a flush water in toilets or urinals. This definition can change depending on the local codes.

Green building: According to the US Environmental Protection Agency (EPA), green building is the practice of creating structures and using processes that are environmentally responsible and resource-efficient throughout a building's life cycle, from siting to design, construction, operation, maintenance, renovation, and deconstruction. This practice expands and complements the classical building design concerns of economy, utility, durability, and comfort.

Green cleaning program : Specifies the green building products to be used (such as products that meet Green Seal, Environmental Choice, or EPA standards), chemicals allowed to be used inside the building, training of the cleaning personnel for the use of chemicals and green cleaning practices, indoor pest control plans, and energy-efficient cleaning equipment.

Green cleaning: The use of environmentally friendly products by also employing environmentally friendly cleaning principles in cleaning.

Green infrastructure: Infrastructure to direct the rainwater collected from the impervious surfaces to the vegetation and soil surfaces without routing them to the storm sewer system.

Green power: Off-site renewable energy.

Green vehicles: Vehicles that achieve a minimum green score of 45 on the American Council for an Energy Efficient Economy (ACEEE) annual vehicle rating guide (or a local equivalent for projects outside the United States.)

Greenfield: The term used to define undeveloped land.

Greenwashing: Refers to the presentation of a product or a material as being more environmentally friendly than it actually is.

Halons: Chemicals used in fire suppression systems.

Hard cost: Costs that physically contribute to the construction, such as labor costs, the cost of construction materials, and equipment.

Health Product Declaration (HPD): Disclosure that provides a product's material ingredients, list of potential chemicals, related concerns, and additional health information.

Heat island effect: Dark colored, nonreflective surfaces absorb heat during hot weather and release it into the atmosphere, and this releasing of heat is called the heat island effect.

Home Energy Rater (HERS Rater): Energy rater credential administered by the Residential Energy Services Network (RESNET).

Home size adjustment (HSA): In the LEED for Homes rating system, points are adjusted in all the categories according to the square footage of the home. Thus, homes that are bigger need to earn more points to achieve a LEED certification while smaller-sized homes can become LEED-certified by earning fewer points. Other LEED rating systems do not have size adjustments.

Impervious surface: A surface that contains less than 50% perviousness.

Indoor air quality management plan: A plan developed to protect the indoor air quality for construction workers and building occupants.

Infill sites: Or infill developments, are sites that at least 75% of their site area were either previously developed or were already being used for other purposes in the urban areas.

Inherently nonemitting materials: Materials with very low or no VOC content.

Integrated pest management (IPM): A sustainable approach that combines knowledge about pests, nature, pest prevention, and control methods that minimize pest infestation and damage while minimizing hazards to the building occupants, the property itself, and the environment.

Integrated process: Emphasizes the importance of connection and communication among all the professionals and stakeholders in the project.

Intensive vegetated roofs: Contain wider variety of plants and which contain more soil depth to support those plants.

Invasive plants: The types of plants that spread and damage the environment by taking over the adjacent existing native and adapted plants.

Land trust: A nonprofit organization that works on conserving lands.

Landscape water requirement (LWR): Is the amount of water that the landscape of the site will require during the site's peak watering month.

LEED AP with specialty: LEED credential, created for professionals with advanced knowledge in green building practices and specialized in a particular LEED rating system.

LEED Campus Program: Used to certify multiple projects that are located on a single campus and which are owned by the same entity.

LEED combined review: A type of LEED certification review in which the documentation for all the design and construction prerequisites/credits are submitted for review at the end of the construction phase (for LEED BD+C and LEED ID+C rating systems).

LEED Fellow: LEED credential created to designate the most exceptional professionals in the green building industry, it is the most prestigious designation awarded.

LEED for Homes Green Rater: Professional who provides in-field verification to LEED for Homes projects. (The other rating systems do not require any in-field verification.)

LEED for Homes Provider Organization: Responsible to oversee all the certification process and incorporate the LEED for Homes rating system requirements into the project's design and construction.

LEED Green Associate: LEED credential created for professionals with a proven, up-to-date understanding of green building principles and practices.

LEED impact categories: Also called system goals, are the key elements that every LEED project aims to accomplish, and it consists of 7 items.

LEED project boundary: Portion of the site submitted for LEED certification. Defined by the platted property line of the project, including all land and water within it.

LEED recertification: Necessary for LEED O+M projects to continue their certification every 5 years. LEED certification granted to projects under the other LEED rating systems do not need a recertification.

LEED split review: A type of LEED certification review in which the design prerequisites/credits are submitted for review during the design phase, and both the additional design prerequisites/credits and all the construction prerequisites/credits are submitted at the end of the construction phase (for LEED BD+C and LEED ID+C rating systems).

LEED Pro Reviewer: Professionals that evaluate the educational LEED courses on EDUCATION @USGBC.

LEED Volume Program: A streamlined certification process for organizations that plan to certify more than 25 prototype-based construction projects within 3 years.

Leverage point: The point where any action taken in the system can bring about significant results.

Life-cycle approach: Evaluates the entire life of a project, product, or service.

Life-cycle assessment (LCA): Evaluates all the environmental effects of a product quantatively for the whole lifetime of that material.

Life-cycle costing (LCC): Assesses a product's total cost for the whole lifetime of the product by evaluating both the initial price and the operating costs.

Light shelves: Are horizontal, light-reflecting overhangs that are positioned to reflect the daylight into the desired area of the building.

Light tubes: Also called sun tubes or sun pipes, are structures that are used to transport sunlight inside a building.

Linear approach: An approach of the conventional building process, in which a project team member completes a work individually and then passes it to the next person.

Load shedding: Is the intentional action by the power utility to reduce the load in the power system in order prevent a total failure of the system.

Load shifting: Is storing the energy generated during off-peak hours, in order to use it during the peak-demand hours.

Long-term bicycle storage: Protected storage from rain and snow for the use of residents and employees.

Low-impact development (LID): An approach to mimic natural systems and to manage the stormwater closest to its source.

Makeup water: Water used to replace the lost water in open systems.

Masking systems: Or sound masking systems, are equipments used to reduce the background noise in spaces.

Minimum efficiency reporting value (MERV): Rates the air filters according to their performance on removing particles from air.

Minimum program requirements (MPRs): Provide guidance on the types of projects that are eligible for LEED certification, protect the integrity of the LEED program, and reduce the number of issues that arise during the certification process.

Monitor based commissioning (MBCx): Is the process of utilizing a software that will monitor real-time data from the building automation system and building meters.

Mulching: A protective layer applied to the surface of soil that will help to keep the roots of the plants cool and therefore prevent evaporation.

Native plants (indigenous plants): Are the type of plants that occur and develop naturally in a specific location.

Natural refrigerants: Refrigerants that occur in nature's biological and chemical cycles without human involvement, such as carbon dioxide (CO_2), water (H_2O), ammonia (NH_3), air, and hydrocarbons such as propane, ethane, and butane.

Negative feedback loops: A change brings an additional change in the opposite direction. If a room gets warmer than the set temperature, the thermostat will send a signal to the air conditioning, and the air conditioning will stop blowing warm air.

Net-zero energy project: A project that only use its own generated renewable energy.

Nonpoint source pollution: Type of pollution in which its source cannot be identified and which generally results from multiple sources.

Nonpotable water: Water that does not meet the human consumption standards.

Nonprocess energy (regulated energy): The energy consumed by the items that are used to condition spaces and maintain comfort and amenities for building occupants.

Open systems: Systems that constantly consume other items, use them, and produce waste at the end.

Open-grid pavement: A pavement system with at least 50% unbound.

Passive daylighting: Is a system that both collects the sunlight using static and nonmoving items such as windows, glass doors, some skylights, light tubes, and light shelves.

Pilot Credits: Credits being tested for the updated version of LEED.

Places of respite: An area in a natural environment, dedicated to connecting patients and visitors, in the hospitals.

Plug loads (receptacle load): Represents the electrical use by all the equipment that is connected to the electrical system via electrical receptacles.

Positive feedback loop: A producing B, which in turn produces more of A. An example of this would be an interest-earning savings account. As the account grows, more interest is earned which in turn brings further account growth.

Postconsumer recycled content: Is the recycled content of a used material. For example, recyclable printer paper can be sent to recycling after being used and can become a part of new printer paper. Other types of materials with postconsumer recycled content can be aluminum cans, water bottles, most glass, wood and steel products, newspapers, and more.

Potable water: Water that is approved for human use that meets or exceeds US Environmental Protection Agency drinking water quality standards (or a local equivalent outside the United States.)

Preconsumer recycled content: Is the content of a material that is recycled before getting used by any consumer. An example may be a sawdust generated during the manufacturing of a wood product that is recycled to be used inside an MDF board (medium density fiberboard).

Preferred parking: Parking spaces that are closest to the main entrance of a building.

Prerequisites: The minimum requirements that all buildings under a certain rating system must meet in order to achieve LEED certification.

Previously developed site: A site that contains at least 75% previously developed land.

Prime farmland: Land that is used for producing food, feed, forage, fiber, and oilseed crops or is available for these uses, as determined by the US Department of Agriculture's Natural Resources Conservation Service.

Prius effect: People can respond to something only if they have real-time information about it.

Process water: Is the type of water used by mechanical or other types of systems in buildings such as cooling towers or medical equipment in hospitals.

Radon: Is a radioactive gas that is naturally found in the soils, rocks, and water bodies that is harmful to human health.

Rainwater harvesting: An aspect of rainwater management that collects and filters the rainwater to be reused as an alternative to potable water.

Rapidly renewable materials: Natural materials that can replenish within 10 years.

Reclaimed water: Is the former blackwater that has been treated and purified for reuse.

Reference soils: Are the native soils of a site.

Refrigerant: Substances used to transfer heat.

Regenerative design: Is a type of building design that creates no waste and also provides more output than consumed input.

Renewable energy certificates (RECs): Or green tags, represent a tradable, nontangible commodity associated with the qualities of renewable energy generation. REC is a proof that, when purchased, an amount of energy was created using renewable energy sources.

Renewable energy: A type of energy that is derived from renewable sources. Renewable energy includes solar, wind, wave, biomass, and geothermal power, plus certain forms of hydropower.

Reverberation time: Is the time span between when a sound is produced and when it dies away.

Scope 1 energy: Relates to the direct energy from the owned or controlled sources.

Scope 2 energy: Energy that relates to the purchased energy.

Scope 3 energy: Relates to the energies that are not owned or directly controlled.

Sensitive lands: Ecologically sensitive areas such as prime farmland, floodplain, habitat, water bodies, or wetland.

Short-term bicycle storage: Typically used by visitors for less than two hours that typically does not provide enclosed parking.

Simple box energy modeling: A preliminary building model used to assess the building's energy loads.

Site assessment: Is a part of the integrative process, which clearly shows the project teams the properties of the site, including its topography, hydrology, climate, soil types, water availability, and human health effects.

Skylights: Are horizontal elements in the roof of the buildings that are made of opaque materials (mostly glass) to allow sunlight into the building.

Smart growth: A neighborhood development approach that protects undeveloped lands and contributes to project development in locations near jobs, schools, shops, and other diverse uses.

Soft cost: Covers everything needed for developing a project that does not physically contribute to the building. All the management and supervision costs, design costs, permits, and taxes can be seen as the soft costs.

Softscape: Part of a landscape that consists of live horticultural elements.

Solar reflectance (SR) value: Shows the solar energy that is reflected by a surface on a scale of 0 to 1. A black surface will have a SR of 0while a white surface will have a SR of 1.

Solar reflectance index (SRI) value: Indicates a material's ability to stay cool by reflecting solar radiation and emitting thermal radiation. Thus, both the solar reflectance and emissivity of a material will be combined to rank the material.

Source reduction: Refers to the exact sizing of the materials to be produced through prefabrication, modular construction, or similar methods, in order to prevent waste.

Spatial daylight autonomy (sDA): Is a metric used to describe annual sufficiency of ambient daylight in building interiors.

Stakeholder meetings: Meetings that are conducted among the project team, stakeholders, neighbors, and community members in order to understand and discuss community needs, issues, and concerns.

Suburban sprawl: The expansion of populations away from central urban areas into low-density areas.

Systems thinking: Refers to the understanding of each and every system of a building while also understanding their relationships and looking at the project as a whole.

Vision glazing: The term used for windows that provide exterior views.

Water balance approach: Aims to balance the water supply with water consumption.

Wet pond (retention pond): Pond designed to hold a specific amount of water indefinitely.

Xeriscaping: Type of landscaping that does not need any irrigation.

Zero-lot project: A type of project which the building footprint covers the whole lot.

INDEX

4

40/60 rule, 33, 281

A

Active daylighting, 220
Active solar, 151
Adapted plants, 94, 95, 102, 104, 110, 127, 129, 131, 288
Adaptive reuse, 184
Addenda, 47
Air quality test, 216, 240
Albedo, 101
Alternative Compliance Path, 40, 208
Alternative daily cover, 195, 209, 210
Alternative fuels, 87
Alternative water sources, 136, 137, 138, 139
Alternative-fuel vehicles, 66, 67
American Council for an Energy-Efficient Economy (ACEEE), 67, 86, 87, 88, 277
Americans with Disabilities Act (ADA), 12
ANSI, 60, 160, 161, 162, 237, 252, 275, 277
Appeals, 50
ASHRAE, 158, 159, 160, 161, 162, 168, 169, 170, 171, 214, 227, 228, 232, 233, 238, 241, 242, 251, 252, 270, 275

B

Backlight-Uplight-Glare (BUG) rating method, 95
Baseline water usage, 124, 145
Basis of design, 60, 156
Bicycle network, 67, 82, 83
Bidding process, 10
Biobased materials, 203, 282
Biofuel, 67, 177, 209, 210
Bioswales, 98, 104
Blackwater, 126, 282, 293
Blowdown, 140, 141
BREEAM, 24

Brownfield remediation, 76
Brownfield sites, 65
Bubbler distribution systems, 127, 129
Budget calculation method, 234, 236
Building automation system, 8, 18, 150, 167, 172, 174, 228, 290
Building envelope commissioning (BECx), 167
Building footprint, 94, 295
Building Information Modeling, 15
Building-related illnesses (BRI), 214
Built environment, 2, 4, 22, 44

C

California Air Resources Board (CARB), 67
Carbon dioxide, 2, 3, 4, 148, 151, 180, 214, 217, 224, 228, 233, 283, 291
Carbon footprint, 151
Carbon neutrality, 151
Carbon offsets, 151, 154, 180, 181
CASBEE, 24
Chain of Custody (CoC) certification, 202
Channel water directly to root systems, 127, 129
Charrettes, 13, 19
Chlorofluorocarbon (CFC), 147, 165, 278
Clerestory windows, 220, 221
Closed system, 6
Closed-loop systems, 126
Combined review, 48
Commingled recycling, 188
Commissioning, 23
Commissioning (Cx) plan, 156
Compact development, 67, 68, 77
Compact fluorescent lights, 149
Composting toilet systems, 126
Compressed workweek, 67, 68
Construction and demolition waste management plan, 194
Conventional building process, 5, 10
Cool pavements, 101
Cool roofs, 101
Corporate Sustainability Reports (CSR), 187, 283
Cradle-to-cradle, 9, 186
Cradle-to-Cradle Certification (C$_2$C), 206
Cradle-to-Cradle Products Innovation Institute, 187

Cradle-to-gate assessment, 187, 200
Cradle-to-grave, 9, 186
Credential Maintenance Program, 26
Credit calculators, 26
Credit Interpretation Rulings, 46
Credit templates, 26
Current facility requirements (CFR), 157
Curtailment event, 173, 284
Custodial effectiveness assessments, 218
Cx plan, 156, 157, 159

D

Daylighting, 147, 157, 219, 220, 221, 222, 224, 245, 281, 291
Demand response, 87, 173, 174, 175, 284
Dematerialization, 186
Department of the Treasury Community Development Financial Institutions Fund Qualified Low-Income Community, 76
Design-bid-build, 10, 14
Design-build, 14
Development footprint, 94
Discovery phase, 19
Diverse uses, 63, 66, 67, 68, 77, 78, 79, 82, 94, 284, 294
DR event, 173, 174
Drip irrigation systems, 127, 129
Dry ponds, 98, 104
Dual-flush toilets, 126
Dwelling unit, 41

E

EDUCATION @USGBC, 26
Efficiencies of scale, 149, 154
Electric vehicle charging stations, 86
Electronic waste, 192, 193
Embodied energy, 9
Emergent properties, 7
Emissivity, 101, 294
Energy audit, 147, 278
Energy Policy Act of 1992, 124, 125, 134, 278
ENERGY STAR, 133, 138, 139, 145, 146, 149, 153, 162, 190, 278
ENERGY STAR Portfolio Manager, 145
ENERGY STAR TargetFinder, 146, 278
Environmental Choice, 189, 190, 217, 286
Environmental Product Declaration (EPD), 187, 285
Environmental Protection Agency, 1, 3, 64, 76, 106, 107, 114, 125, 131, 136, 137, 149, 277, 279, 286, 292, 304, 305
Erosion and sedimentation control (ESC) plan, 16, 106, 277
Evapotranspiration, 95
Exemplary performance, 256, 257, 258
Expedited review, 50
Extended Producer Responsibility (EPR), 203, 279, 285
Extensive vegetated roofs, 113

F

Facility manager, 13, 14
Fairtrade, 189
Federal Emergency Management Agency (FEMA), 73
Federal Empowerment Zone site, 75
Federal Enterprise Community site, 75
Federal Renewal Community site, 75
Feedback loops, 6, 7, 8, 12, 291
Final construction review, 49
Final construction verification visit, 52
Final Cx report, 156, 157, 158, 159
Final design review, 49
Fixture schedules, 132, 134
Floor hazard areas, 94
Floorscore, 216
Floor-to-area ratio, 65
Flow fixtures, 127
Flush-out, 217, 224, 239, 240
Food Alliance, 189
Forest Stewardship Council (FSC), 202, 204, 205, 279
Full-time equivalent (FTE) value, 124

G

GBCI, 14, 24, 25, 26, 27
Gbtool, 24
Geothermal heat pumps, 151
Glare, 95, 104, 119, 120, 121, 167, 219, 221, 222, 245, 248, 282
Glare-control devices, 245
Global climate change, 4, 43, 44
Global warming potentials (GWP), 178
Graywater, 59, 126, 127, 129, 136, 137, 138, 139, 281, 286
Green Building Initiative (GBI), 24
Green chemistry, 206
Green cleaning program, 217, 218
Green Globes, 24
Green housekeeping program, 18
Green infrastructure (GI), 98, 115
Green Label, 216
Green Label Plus, 216
Green power, 176, 180, 278, 287
Green pricing, 150
Green purchasing, 18
Green Seal, 189, 190, 216, 217, 286
Green vehicles, 66, 67, 68, 86, 87, 277
Greenbuild International Conference & Expo, 22
Green-e, 151, 180, 181, 278
GREENGUARD, 216
Greenhouse gas emissions, 4, 5
Greenscreen, 206, 207, 208, 279
Greenwashing, 187, 190
Guiding principles, 22

H

Halons, 165, 166
Hard costs, 17
Harvested rainwater, 126, 127, 129
Health Product Declaration (HPD), 187, 287
Heat island effect, 64, 100, 101, 104, 108, 116, 118, 287
High priority site, 75
High-efficiency toilets, 126
High-intensity discharge lamps, 149
Home Energy Rating System Rater (HERS Rater), 52
Home Energy Saver, 147, 278
Home size adjustment (HSA), 147
Hydrocarbons, 148, 283, 291
Hydrochlorofluorocarbon (HCFC), 147, 278
Hydrofluorocarbons, 179

I

Illuminating Engineering Society of North America (IESNA), 95, 277
Impact Categories, 43
Incandescent lights, 149
Indigenous plants, 95, 131, 291
Indoor air quality management plan, 16, 224, 237
In-field verification, 25, 39, 51, 52, 289
Infill sites, 65
Inherently nonemitting materials, 216
Integrated Pest Management (IPM), 102, 104
Integrated process, 5, 10, 11, 12, 16, 19
Intensive vegetated roofs, 113
International Code Council (ICC), 12, 24
International Green Construction Code (IGCC),, 24
International Society of Arboriculture (ISA), 73
International Union for Conservation of Nature Red List, 73
Invasive plants, 95, 288
Irrigation, 8, 11
Iterative process, 12, 19

L

Land Trust Alliance, 111
Land-cleaning debris, 195
Landscape water requirement, 125, 131
LEED AP, 14, 22, 25, 26
LEED Campus, 53, 288
LEED Fellow, 25
LEED for Homes Green Raters, 25
LEED for Homes Provider Organization, 52
LEED for Homes Scope and Eligibility Guidelines, 41
LEED for Homes workbook, 52
LEED Green Associate, 14, 22, 25, 32, 265, 267, 268, 270, 289
LEED Green Building Rating System, 22
LEED Interpretations, 46
LEED Online, 26, 27

LEED Pilot Credit Library, 43
LEED Professional Credentials, 25
LEED Project Administrator, 14
LEED project boundary, 41
LEED rating system adaptations, 40
LEED rating systems, 26, 29, 30, 32, 40, 46, 47, 51, 147, 255, 268, 287, 289
LEED Reference Guide, 46
LEED Scorecard, 31
LEED Volume, 53, 289
Legacy LEED AP, 25
Leverage point, 8
Life-cycle, 6, 8, 22, 23
Life-cycle approach, 6, 8, 9
Life-cycle assessment, 9, 15, 19, 190, 196, 197, 198, 200
Life-cycle costing, 9
Life-cycle thinking, 5
Light shelves, 220, 290
Light trespass, 95, 104, 119, 121
Light tubes, 220, 290
Light-Emitting Diodes (LEDs), 149
Lighting boundary, 121
Linear approach, 13
Load shedding, 174, 175
Load shifting, 174, 175
Local codes, 12
Location valuation factor, 186, 199, 201, 204, 205
Long-term bicycle storage, 83
Low-flow showerheads, 126
Low-impact development, 98, 104, 114, 115

M

Makeup water, 126, 133, 140, 141
Marine Stewardship Council Blue Eco-Label, 189
Masking systems, 251, 252, 290
Methane, 4, 214
Midconstruction verification visit, 52
Minimum efficiency reporting value (MERV), 218
Minimum Program Requirements, 40
Mixed-mode ventilation, 217
Monitor-based commissioning (MBCx), 167
Montreal Protocol, 147, 165, 166, 178, 278
Mulching, 96, 127, 291

N

National Institute of Building Sciences (NIBS), 169, 278
Native plants, 95, 291
Natural refrigerants, 148, 179
Natural Resources Conservation Service (NCRS) soil survey, 72
Natural ventilation, 147, 149, 154, 217, 227, 228
NatureServe, 73, 74
Negative feedback loops, 7
Net-zero energy, 3
New Buildings Institute, 3, 145, 146
NIBS Guideline, 158

Nonpoint source pollution, 97
Nonprocess energy, 160, 161, 162
Nonprocess loads, 161, 162

O

Occupancy sensors, 149, 154, 222
Occupant surveys, 18
Off-site renewable energy, 150, 287
On-site renewable energy, 150
On-site water retention, 97
Open systems, 6
Open-grid paving, 97, 101
Operations and maintenance (O&M) plan, 156, 157
Optional prerequisite review, 51
Owner's project requirements, 60, 153, 154, 156, 158, 282, 283
Ozone, 4, 147, 165, 166, 178, 179, 187, 198, 199, 201, 240, 285
Ozone depletion potentials (ODP), 178

P

Parking Consultants Council, 85, 277
Passive daylighting, 220
Passive solar, 151
Performance testing, 51, 52, 285
Pervious paving, 97
Photosensors, 149, 154
Pilot credit library, 257
Pilot credits, 40, 43, 258, 291
Plug loads, 160, 162
Positive feedback loop, 7
Postconstruction verification, 168, 169
Postconsumer recycled content, 202, 292
Precertification, 34, 51
Preconsumer recycled content, 202, 292
Predesign phase, 6, 11, 14
Preliminary construction review, 49
Preliminary design review, 49
Preliminary water budget analysis, 59
Prerequisites, 42
Preventive maintenance program, 153, 154
Prime farmland, 65, 72, 94, 292
Prius effect, 8
Process energy, 160, 161, 162
Process load, 58, 160
Process water, 98, 126, 138, 139, 142
PV panels, 118, 151

R

Radon, 214, 218, 224
Rainforest Alliance Certification, 189
Rainwater, 11
Rainwater harvesting, 98, 293
Rapidly renewable materials, 186, 190

REACH Optimization, 206, 208, 279
Receptacle loads, 160
Re-certification, 18
Reclaimed water, 126, 127, 129, 138, 139, 281
Reference soils, 111
Reflective paving materials, 95
Refrigerants, 42, 146, 147, 148, 154, 165, 166, 178, 179, 278, 291
Regenerative design, 3, 293
Regulated energy, 160, 162, 291
Renewable energy, 3, 150, 154, 158, 160, 168, 170, 173, 176, 177, 180, 187, 256, 291, 293
Renewable Energy Certificates (RECs), 150, 180
Residential Energy Services Network (RESNET), 52
Retrocommissioning, 150, 153, 154
Reverberation time, 251, 252
Royal Astronomical Society of Canada's light-abatement recommendations, 103

S

SBTool, 24
Scope 1 Energy, 5
Scope 2 Energy, 5
Scope 3 Energy, 5
Sensitive lands, 39, 65, 68, 72, 75, 262
Sheet Metal and Air Conditioning National Contractors Association (SMACNA), 216, 237, 279
Shortest path analysis, 89
Short-term bicycle storage, 83
Sick building syndrome (SBS), 214
Simple box energy modeling, 58
Single-occupancy vehicles, 11
Site assessment, 94, 104, 108, 109
Skylights, 220, 294
Small task groups, 13, 19
Smart growth, 37, 63, 64, 65, 68, 70
Soft costs, 17
Solar panels, 101
Solar reflectance, 101, 116, 117, 294
Solar reflectance index, 101, 116, 117
Source control, 214, 232, 233
Source reduction, 185, 190, 194
Source separation, 194
South Coast Air Quality Management District (SCAQMD), 216
Spatial daylight autonomy (sDA), 245, 246, 248
Split review, 48
Stakeholder meetings, 13, 19
Stormwater pollution prevention plan, 16
Suburban sprawl, 38, 64, 65, 67
Sustainable material purchasing program, 189
Sustainable site management plan, 102
System goals, 43
Systems thinking, 5, 6, 7, 8

T

Task lighting, 222

Team meeting, 13
Team meetings, 13, 19
Telecommuting, 67, 68
Thermal comfort, 58, 219, 241, 242, 275
Thermal mass, 147, 148
Tidal power, 152
Transportation demand management strategies, 84
Triple bottom line, 3, 4, 16, 19, 22, 268

U

Unregulated energy, 160, 162
Uplighting, 95, 104
US Department of Energy's Commercial Buildings Energy
    Consumption Survey (CBECS), 176, 177, 181, 278
US Department of Housing and Urban Development's Qualified
    Census Tracts (QCT), 76
US Endangered Species Act, 73
USDA Organic, 189
USGBC, 14, 21, 22, 24, 25, 26, 53
USGBC's Mission, 22
USGBC's Vision, 22

V

Vegetated roofs, 97, 101, 112, 113, 116, 285, 288
Vehicle miles traveled, 38

Vision glazing, 222, 249
Volatile organic compounds (VOCs), 214, 215, 234, 240

W

Waste management plan, 17, 188, 195, 209
Waste-to-energy systems, 209
Water balance approach, 123
Water bodies, 16, 65, 72, 73, 96, 218, 285, 292, 293
Waterless urinals, 126
Watersense, 125, 126, 131, 132, 134, 136, 137, 278, 279
Watersense Water Budget Tool, 125, 131, 136, 137, 279
Wave energy converters (WEC), 152
Weather-based irrigation controllers, 127, 129
Wetlands, 16, 65, 73, 94, 96, 108, 285

X

Xeriscaping, 127, 129, 130, 131

Z

Zero Emission Vehicles, 67
Zero-lot-line projects, 65

REFERENCES

CHAPTER 1

1   J.F. Kenny, N.L. Barber, S.S. Hutson, K.S. Linsey, J.K. Lovelace, & M.A. Maupin. Estimated use of water in the United States in 2005: US Geological Survey Circular 1344, (2009).

2   D.M. Roodman & N. Lenssen "A Building Revolution: How Ecology and Health Concerns Are Transforming Construction," Worldwatch Paper 124 (Worldwatch Institute, 1995).

3   Energy Information Administration, EIA Annual Energy Outlook (EIA, 2008).

4   US Department of Energy Annual Outlook 2008.

5   Turner, C. & Frankel, Energy Performance of LEED for New Construction Buildings (2008), http://www.newbuildings.org/sites/default/files/Energy_Performance_of_LEED-NC_Buildings-Final_3-4-08b.pdf.

6   US Environmental Protection Agency, Report to Congress on Indoor Air Quality, volume 2, EPA/400/1-89/001C (EPA, 1989).

CHAPTER 5

1   US Environmental Protection Agency, http://www2.epa.gov/smartgrowth/about-smart-growth.

2   US Energy Information Administration, Emissions of Greenhouse Gases Report (December 8, 2009), http://www.eia.doe.gov/oiaf/1605/ggrpt/.

3   International Council on Clean Transportation, Passenger Vehicles, (accessed March 22, 2013).

4   EPA, http://www.epa.gov/climatechange/ghgemissions/sources/transportation.html.

CHAPTER 6

1   Yang, X., Y.Hou, and B. Chen, Observed Surface Warming Induced by Urbanization in East China, J. Geophys. Res., 116(2011), D14113, doi:10.1029/2010JD015452.

CHAPTER 8

1   C. Turner and M. Frankel, Energy Performance of LEED for New Construction Buildings (March 4, 2008), http://www.newbuildings.org/sites/default/files/Energy_Performance_of_LEED-NC_Buildings-Final_3-4-08b.pdf.

2   "Energy Consumption Characteristics of Commercial Buildings HVAC Systems Volume III: Energy Savings Potential" – US Department of Energy.

CHAPTER 9

1   US Environmental Protection Agency, http://epa.gov/osw/conserve/rrr/imr/cdm/pubs/cd-meas.pdf.

2   US Environmental Protection Agency, http://epa.gov/osw/nonhaz/municipal/pubs/msw2009rpt.pdf.

3   "Healthy Business Strategies for Transforming the Toxic Chemical Economy," Clean Production Action (2006), http://www.cleanproduction.org/library/CPA-Healthybusiness-1.pdf.

4   Anastas and Warner, Green Chemistry: Theory and Practice (New York: Oxford University Press, 2000)

CHAPTER 10

1   Wyon, D. 1996. "Individual Microclimate Control: Required Range, Probable Benefits, and Current Feasibility." In Proceedings of Indoor Air 1996: Seventh International Conference of Indoor Air Quality and Climate, vol.1, Nagoya, Japan, pp.1067-1072.

2   Boyce, Peter, Reviews of Technical Reports on Daylight and Productivity (Rensselaer Polytechnic Institute, 2004); Heschong Mahone Group, Daylighting in Schools: An Investigation into the Relationship between Daylighting and Human Performance (1999).

3   Edwards, L., and P. Torcellini. A Literature Study of the Effects of Natural Light on Building Occupants (Golden, Colorado: NREL, 2002).

4   Ulrich, Roger, et al., "A Review of the Research Literature on Evidence-Based Healthcare Design," Health Environments Research and Design Journal 1(3) (2008), (http://www.herdjournal.com).